THE ILLUSTRATED ENCYCLOPEDIA OF

MAMMALS

THE ILLUSTRATED ENCYCLOPEDIA OF
MAMMALS

ANDROMEDA

THE ILLUSTRATED ENCYCLOPEDIA OF
MAMMALS

Consultant Editor: Andrew Branson
Managing Editor: Lionel Bender
Art Editor: Ben White
Designers: Malcolm Smythe, Ben White
Text Editors: Miles Litvinoff, Madeleine
   Samuel, Barbara Taylor-Cork
Production: Clive Sparling

Media conversion and typesetting:
Robert and Peter MacDonald,
   Una Macnamara

Planned and produced by
Andromeda Oxford Ltd
11–15 The Vineyard, Abingdon,
Oxfordshire OX14 3PX

Copyright © Andromeda Oxford Ltd 1993

ISBN 1 871869 16 1

Published in Great Britain by
Andromeda Oxford Ltd
This edition specially produced for
Selectabook Ltd

Origination by Alpha Reprographics Ltd,
England

Printed in Hong Kong by Dai Nippon Ltd

Authors:
Martyn Bramwell
Robin Kerrod
Christopher O'Toole
Steve Parker
John Stidworthy

CONTENTS

INTRODUCTION

The *Illustrated Encyclopedia of Mammals* provides an ideal introduction to one of the most successful groups of animals. It covers a wide spectrum of species, from the grey whale to tiny rodents. *The Illustrated Encyclopedia of Mammals* begins by explaining what a mammal is. The encyclopedia then includes entries on mammals such as squirrels, beavers, and rabbits. Compared to mammals like elephants and rhinoceroses, the majority of these animals are small. Nevertheless their life-styles are intriguing. Some, such as voles, burrow. Others, such as tree squirrels, climb. Some species of rats and mice live close to people. All these animals are herbivores, which means they eat plant material as the main part of their diet. But their diets vary greatly. Beavers feed on wood and gerbils on seeds, while the koala eats only eucalyptus leaves and the honey possum feeds solely on nectar. Also included in the encyclopedia are herbivores that are much larger, such as zebras and rhinoceroses, and carnivores, such as otters and cheetahs.

The past 65 million years has often been called the "Age of Mammals". During the time of the dinosaurs, mammals were small and nocturnal. But when the dinosaurs became extinct, mammals began to replace the reptiles as the dominant large land animals. They evolved into many different species with many different roles, from tiny burrowing seed-eaters to large predators. Great hordes of grass-eating mammals wandered across the plains of the northern continents; carnivores, such as sabre-toothed tigers, hunted in packs feeding on abundant prey. In some regions, enormous forms of some of our modern-day mammals developed. The spectacular Indricotherium, an Asian relative of the rhinoceros, was 5.5 metres high and was one of the largest land mammals that has ever lived. It browsed on the high branches of trees, rather like the present-day giraffe. In South America, there were giant sloths and armadillos.

During the last million years, the mammal world has seen tremendous changes. A series of Ice Ages, spreading from the North Pole, has forced mammals to retreat southwards. The cold steppes were inhabited by such mammals as woolly mammoths, giant elks, woolly rhinoceroses, bison and cave bears. These great communities of mammals are now largely extinct, with only a few herds of bison still remaining. The cause of their extinction is thought to be due, in main, to another mammal – humans. Around 15,000 years ago, tribes began to hunt the mammals of these regions and, by about 10,000 years ago, most had been hunted to the point of extinction. Humans have continued to contribute to local and global extinctions ever since, with creatures such as the giant lemur, from Madagascar, the quagga, a type of zebra from Southern Africa, and Steller's sea cow, from the North Pacific, all disappearing in the last few centuries. Today, we are much more aware of our effect on the wildlife around us, however there are concerns over the fate of once common species such as the black rhinoceros, African elephant and many of the great whales.

Humans have always had a close relationship with other mammals; cave paintings show herds of bison and antelope. From the earliest times, it is probable that dogs were domesticated to help round up game. Pastoral farming with sheep and cattle has been carried out for thousands of years, and until this century, the horse provided humans with their main means of land transport. Because of this long association, our knowledge of the mammals around us and how they live is probably better than of any other group of animals. Research by specialists continues today and provides the basis of much of the information in this encyclopedia.

Each article in this encyclopedia is devoted to an individual species or group of closely related species. The text starts with a short scene-setting story that highlights one or more the animal's unique features. It then continues with details of the most interesting aspects of the animal's physical features and abilities, diet and feeding behaviour, and general life-style. It also covers conservation and the animal's relationships with people.

Fact Panel
The "Fact Panel" consists of the various symbols that appear throughout the book. These symbols summarize key characteristics of a species or a group of species. A black circle, for example, indicates an animal or groups of animals that is active primarily at night, such as bats, whereas a red circle indicates an animal or group of animals that is active during the day, beavers for example. Other symbols describe such characteristics as "Group size",

Conservation status", "Habitat", "Diet" and "Breeding". Range maps indicate where particular animals dwell.

The symbols and maps give the reader an immediate grasp of the key elements of an animal's behaviour and its chances of surviving. One can tell at a glance whether to expect the species to be found in large herds in dry grassy plains or solitarily in a forest. The "Fact Panel" symbols are a form of naturalist's shorthand, a way of organizing mammals by their habitat and, in terms of their relationship with the world's environment, by their probable fate.

Fact Box

Each entry contains a "Fact Box" which uses the symbols that appear in the "Fact Panel". The symbols denoting habitat, activity time and diet, for example, appear in the "Fact Box". The "Fact Box" also includes a range map.

The "Fact Box" includes a list of the common and scientific names (Latin) names of species mentioned in each entry's main text and photo captions. For species illustrated in major artwork panels but not described elsewhere, the names are given in the caption accompanying the artwork. In such illustrations, animals are shown to scale unless otherwise stated; actual dimensions may be found in the text.

Comparison Silhouettes

In addition to the descriptive symbols in the "Fact Panel", in many cases the encyclopedia suggests the relative size of animals by comparing them to an average-size human being, or part thereof. It is difficult to imagine how big a koala is, or a grey whale, or a hippopotamus. But when you look at a picture of a dormouse next to a human foot, you can tell immediately how big it is. Comparison silhouettes appear in the upper right-hand corner of most pages in this encyclopedia.

FACT PANEL: Key to symbols denoting general features of animals

SYMBOLS WITH NO WORDS

Activity time

● Nocturnal

● Daytime

◐ Dawn/Dusk

○ All the time

Group size

◰ Solitary

▦ Pairs

◧ Small groups (up to 10)

■ Large groups

◪ Variable

Conservation status

☠ All species threatened

☠ Some species threatened

No species threatened (no symbol)

SYMBOLS NEXT TO HEADINGS

Habitat

◣ General

◣ Mountain/Moorland

◺ Desert

〰 Sea

▣ Amphibious

◿ Tundra

◸ Forest/Woodland

● Grassland

≋ Freshwater

Diet

▣ Other animals

▣ Plants

◿ Animals and Plants

Breeding

◎ Seasonal (at fixed times)

◍ Non-seasonal (at any time)

WHAT IS A MAMMAL?

The mammals are one of the most successful groups of animals. They are found in almost every habitat, from the Arctic tundra to the Sahara Desert, from the oceans to the mountaintops. One group of mammals, the bats, has even taken to the air.

Mammals are vertebrates: they have an internal bony skeleton for support. The backbone is made up of a series of bony units called vertebrae. A bony shoulder girdle and pelvic girdle are attached to the backbone. A pair of forelegs is attached to the shoulder girdle and a pair of hind legs to the pelvic girdle (see illustration below).

Unlike fish, reptiles and amphibians (other vertebrate groups), mammals are able to keep their inside temperature fairly constant by producing the heat they need from their own body processes. Scientists now use the term endotherm to describe this type of animal rather than the more familiar term warm-blooded, which can be misleading. The blood of so-called cold-blooded animals, such as frogs

▲ A Cape fox vixen suckles her cubs. The supply of milk helps to give the young a good start in life by providing the necessary food for growth.

and snakes, is cold if their surroundings are cold, but after sunbathing their blood may actually be hotter than the blood of warm-blooded mammals. Being able to control their body temperature regardless of the temperature of their surroundings has allowed the mammals to colonize most parts of the globe. Birds are also endotherms.

MAMMALS' SPECIAL FEATURES

The two main features that distinguish mammals from other vertebrates are hair and milk. Hairs trap a layer of air next to the skin. Air does not easily allow heat to pass through it, so this helps the mammal to stay warm.

When mammals reproduce, the female produces milk from special mammary glands and releases it through nipples on her belly. The milk forms a complete food for the baby mammal until it is strong enough to find food for itself. Milk production has allowed some mammals to give birth to young which may be small and helpless. These mammals can produce more young at a time than if the young had to be independent at birth. Because the young spend a long time with their parents while they grow up, this provides an opportunity to learn from experience and improves their chances of survival.

The mammal skull contains a large brain. The cerebral hemispheres of the brain (the parts dealing with consciousness, mental ability and intelligence) are very large.

The lower jaw is formed from a single bone, which makes it very strong. Mammal teeth are usually of various shapes and sizes, specialized for particular diets. A bony plate, the secondary palate, separates the nose passages from the mouth cavity, allowing a mammal to breathe when its mouth is full. This means that a mammal can spend as much time as it likes chewing its food before swallowing it. Most other vertebrates have to

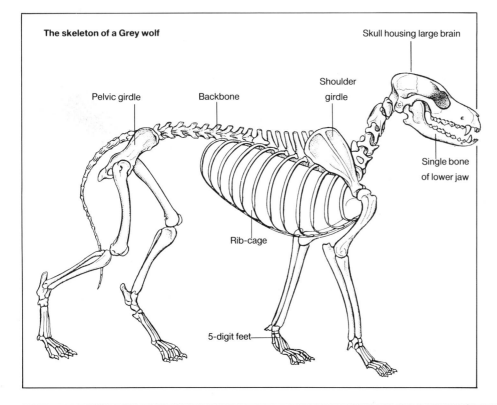

The skeleton of a Grey wolf

Pelvic girdle

Backbone

Shoulder girdle

Skull housing large brain

Single bone of lower jaw

Rib-cage

5-digit feet

swallow their food whole, or they would run out of breath.

The mammal body is divided by a sheet of muscle, the diaphragm, at the base of the rib cage. Movements of the diaphragm help the animal breathe efficiently. Contraction of the diaphragm, along with moving of the ribs, sucks air into the lungs. The reverse process pushes air out of the lungs.

TYPES OF MAMMALS
There are three classes of mammals, distinguished by the way in which they breed (as shown below).

The Monotremes
These are the egg-laying mammals. They are the most primitive mammals. There are only three species: the duck-billed platypus and two kinds of echidna or spiny anteater. Monotremes are found only in Australia and New Guinea. They lay eggs with leathery shells, rather like those of reptiles. These hatch into tiny, little-developed young. Monotremes have no nipples. The young cling to the fur on their mother's belly and suck at the milk oozing out of the skin where the milk glands open to the surface.

The Marsupials
In this class, which includes the kangaroos, the koala and the opossums, the young develop inside the mother's womb, but are born at a very early stage of development. At birth, they look rather like tiny grubs. They climb up their mother's fur into a pouch on her belly. Inside the pouch are nipples which produce milk.

The Placental Mammals
This is the largest and most "advanced" group of mammals. The young develop inside their mother's womb attached to a placenta. This is a special structure which supplies them with food and oxygen from the mother's blood and carries away their waste products. This food supply allows the young to reach a more advanced stage before being born. Placental mammal mothers produce milk from nipples on their bellies.

▼Some young mammals, like this new-born gazelle, can stand soon after birth.

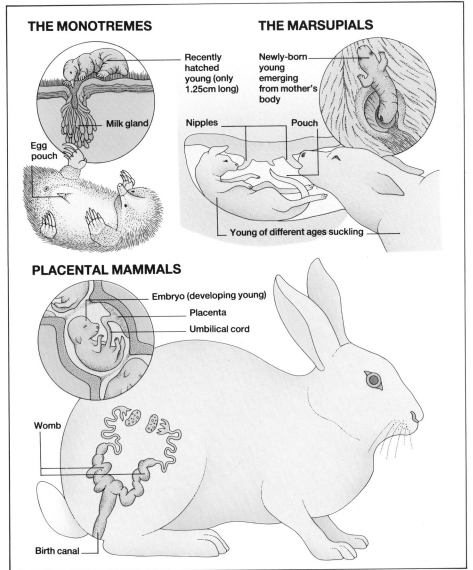

THE MONOTREMES

Recently hatched young (only 1.25cm long)

Milk gland

Egg pouch

THE MARSUPIALS

Newly-born young emerging from mother's body

Nipples

Pouch

Young of different ages suckling

PLACENTAL MAMMALS

Embryo (developing young)

Placenta

Umbilical cord

Womb

Birth canal

11

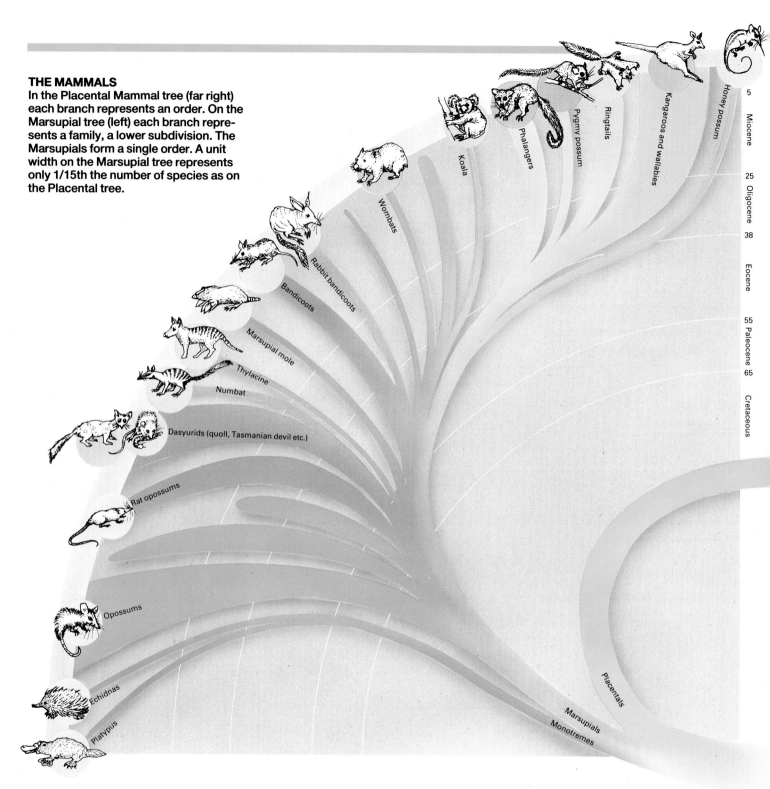

THE MAMMALS
In the Placental Mammal tree (far right) each branch represents an order. On the Marsupial tree (left) each branch represents a family, a lower subdivision. The Marsupials form a single order. A unit width on the Marsupial tree represents only 1/15th the number of species as on the Placental tree.

Honey possum

Kangaroos and wallabies

Ringtails

Pygmy possum

Phalangers

Koala

Wombats

Rabbit bandicoots

Bandicoots

Marsupial mole

Thylacine

Numbat

Dasyurids (quoll, Tasmanian devil etc.)

Rat opossums

Opossums

Echidnas

Platypus

Placentals

Marsupials

Monotremes

Miocene 5
Oligocene 25
Eocene 38
Paleocene 55
65
Cretaceous

CLASSIFYING THE MAMMALS

There are over 4,000 different species of mammal, around 1,000 genera and 135 families. Mammals are grouped into Monotremes (3 species), Marsupials (266) and Placental mammals (over 3,750, of which a quarter are bats). They can be further sorted according to their body structure, especially the number, shapes and arrangement of the bones and teeth.

Each mammal's body is suited it to its particular way of life. Thus cheetahs have long legs and flexible backbones

▲This mammal family tree shows how the mammals have increased in variety with time. The ancestors of the mammals first appeared on Earth about 300 million years ago. Since then, mammals have evolved a wide range of feeding habits and life-styles, allowing them to spread to most parts of the globe.

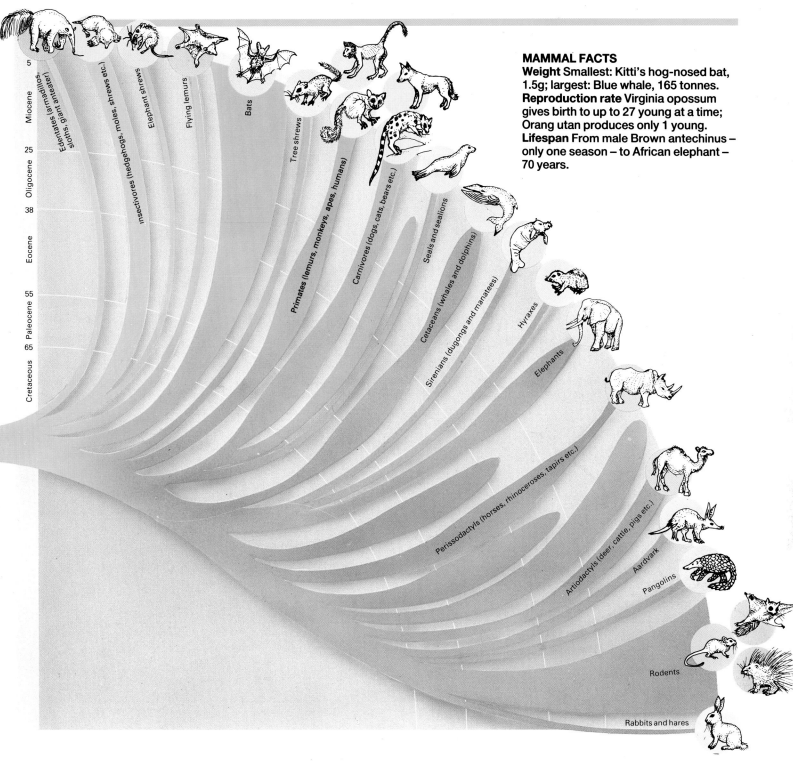

Miocene
5

25
Oligocene
38
Eocene

55
Paleocene
65
Cretaceous

Edentates (armadillos, sloths, giant anteater)

Insectivores (hedgehogs, moles, shrews etc.)

Elephant shrews

Flying lemurs

Bats

Tree shrews

Primates (lemurs, monkeys, apes, humans)

Carnivores (dogs, cats, bears etc.)

Seals and sealions

Cetaceans (whales and dolphins)

Sirenians (dugongs and manatees)

Hyraxes

Elephants

Perissodactyls (horses, rhinoceroses, tapirs etc.)

Artiodactyls (deer, cattle, pigs etc.)

Aardvark

Pangolins

Rodents

Rabbits and hares

During these 300 million years, the continents have moved around the globe, and the climate has changed. Not all the mammals that arose were successful. Some branches of the tree do not reach to the present day. Others, like the rodents and bats, are still expanding and changing today.

for chasing after prey, seals have flippers for swimming, and bats have wings for flying.

A mammal's jaws and teeth reveal how it feeds. Lions have special sharp teeth for seizing prey, tearing flesh and crushing bones. Sheep have large flat teeth for grinding leaves. Baleen whales have huge plate-like sieves for filtering sea water.

Classifying the mammals according to their body structure naturally arranges them in groups with similar life styles and feeding habits.

ECHIDNAS

A female echidna is resting quietly in her burrow. Inside her pouch is a small, soft, leathery egg, which she laid 10 days ago. The egg starts to move and soon splits open. A tiny form no bigger than a peanut crawls out. It makes its way to the milk glands in the mother's pouch and starts to suckle.

The echidna is one of the most unusual of all mammals because it lays eggs. The only other mammal to do this is the platypus. Both these mammals are called monotremes, a word meaning "one hole". They have a single opening, not two, at the rear of the body.

SPINY COAT

There are two species of echidna. The smaller species, with the shorter snout, is the Short-beaked or Common echidna. It looks rather like a hedgehog. It has long sharp spines sticking out of thick dark fur. The spiny coat hides a short tail and also covers ear-slits just behind the bulging eyes.

The Short-beaked echidna is found throughout Australia and Tasmania and also on the island of New Guinea to the north. It lives in almost all kinds of habitat, from dry desert to rain forest and snowy mountains.

The Long-beaked echidna is also found in New Guinea, but only in highland regions. It has longer fur than its Short-beaked relative. It also has fewer and shorter spines, which are usually visible only at the sides and on the head.

In both species the males are heavier than the females. Males have a horny spur on the ankle of the hind limbs, which they use when fighting.

DIET OF ANTS AND WORMS

Echidnas are often called spiny anteaters. But only the Short-beaked species eat ants and termites. The Long-beaked echidna feeds mainly on earthworms. Like the anteaters, however, echidnas have no teeth. The Short-beaked echidna takes ants and termites with its long tongue, made

ECHIDNAS Tachyglossidae
(*2 species*)

■ Habitat: semi-desert to highlands.

■ Diet: ants, termites, earthworms.

◎ Breeding: young hatched from 1 egg after about 10 days incubation.

Size: Short-beaked echidna: head-body 30cm, weight 2.5kg; Long-beaked echidna: head-body 90cm, weight 10kg.

Colour: black to brown coat, with paler-coloured spines.

Lifespan: up to 50 years in captivity.

Species mentioned in text:
Long-beaked echidna (*Zaglossus bruijni*)
Short-beaked or Common echidna (*Tachyglossus aculeatus*)

▲The long naked snout of the Long-beaked echidna curves downwards. The mouth at the tip is tiny. It can be opened just wide enough to allow the tongue to pass through.

▶When swimming, the Short-beaked echidna uses its snout as a snorkel, pushing the tip into the air to breathe.

▲The nostrils of a Short-beaked echidna are much larger than its mouth. The eyes are bulging. The powerful forelimbs are tipped with tough claws for digging.

sticky with saliva. The insects are crushed between spines at the back of the tongue and the roof of the mouth. The Long-beaked echidna catches earthworms in spines that run in a groove in its tongue. It then draws the worms into its tiny mouth, head or tail first.

►With only its spines showing, a Short-beaked echidna digs into an ants' nest. In soft soil echidnas may bury themselves to shelter from the Sun's heat.

PLATYPUS

The dog sniffing around near the river bank suddenly gives an excited bark. It makes a short dash and pounces on a small furry creature, which has the bill of a duck and the flat tail of a beaver. This odd-looking creature is a platypus – unfortunately for the dog, a male. The platypus wriggles this way and that and then manages to jab the dog with the spurs on its hind legs. They deliver a powerful venom. Startled and in pain, the dog drops the platypus, which escapes into the river.

The platypus is the only mammal besides certain shrews that is venomous. But only the male is able to produce and deliver the poison, which can kill a dog and cause agonizing pain to human beings.

The platypus is also most unusual among mammals because it reproduces by laying and hatching eggs. When the young hatch, they feed on their mother's milk, like all mammals do. The only other mammals to lay eggs are the echidnas, which together with the platypus make up the animal order of monotremes.

The platypus is found in eastern Australia. It lives in burrows in the banks of rivers and lakes, spending much of its time in the water. Once hunted nearly to extinction for its fur, the platypus is now protected and thriving.

SLEEK SWIMMER

The platypus moves awkwardly on the land on its short legs. But in the water it is swift and graceful. Its body, covered with short thick fur, becomes beautifully streamlined, and it propels itself with its broad webbed forefeet. It steers with its partly webbed hind feet and flat tail.

When walking on land, the platypus

folds back the webbing on its forefeet. This exposes thick nails, which the platypus uses for digging its burrows.

FEEDING AND BREEDING

When the platypus dives into water, it closes its eyes and ears. Under water the platypus's soft, rubbery and skin-covered bill becomes its eyes and ears. The bill is very sensitive to touch, which helps the animal find its food as

▼The female platypus digs a breeding burrow where she will lay her eggs and raise her young. The young suckle her and remain in the burrow for up to 4 months.

▲The platypus is often called the duck-bill. But unlike a duck's bill the bill of the platypus is soft and flexible.

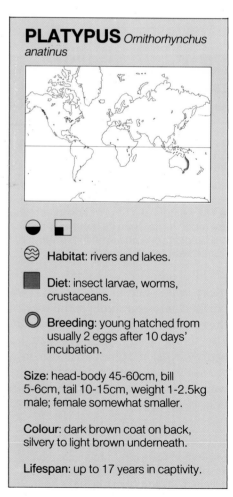

PLATYPUS *Ornithorhynchus anatinus*

◑ ◨

〰 Habitat: rivers and lakes.

■ Diet: insect larvae, worms, crustaceans.

◯ Breeding: young hatched from usually 2 eggs after 10 days' incubation.

Size: head-body 45-60cm, bill 5-6cm, tail 10-15cm, weight 1-2.5kg male; female somewhat smaller.

Colour: dark brown coat on back, silvery to light brown underneath.

Lifespan: up to 17 years in captivity.

▲The platypus feeds mainly on the river bottom. It uses its sensitive bill to sift through the mud and gravel for insect larvae and small shellfish.

it searches for food on the river bed.

The platypus scoops up insect larvae and crustaceans in its bill, then stores them in its two cheek pouches, located just behind the bill. The platypus has no teeth, but inside the cheek pouches are horny ridges which help grind the food into smaller pieces.

It is thought that platypuses mate in the water after the female slowly approaches the male and he then chases her and grasps her tail. Some days later the female starts to dig a long breeding burrow. She makes at the end a cosy nesting chamber, lined with grass and leaves. There she lays up to three soft, leathery eggs and keeps them warm.

In about 10 days the young hatch and crawl to the mammary glands on the mother's belly and start to suck the milk-soaked fur there.

OPOSSUMS

OPOSSUMS Didelphidae
(*75 species*)

● ■

Habitat: mainly wooded areas in temperate and tropical regions.

Diet: grass, fruit, insects, snakes, birds, other small animals, carrion.

Breeding: many young after pregnancy of about 2 weeks; up to about 10 young successfully raised.

Size: smallest (Formosan mouse opossum): head-body 5.5cm, tail 4.2cm, weight 10g; largest (Virginia opossum): up to head-body 55cm, tail 54cm, weight 5.5kg.

Colour: grey, brown and golden coat, sometimes striped.

Lifespan: up to about 3 years, longer in captivity.

Species mentioned in text:
Brown four-eyed opossum
    (*Metachirus nudicaudatus*)
Formosan mouse opossum
    (*Marmosa formosa*)
Little water opossum or lutrine
    (*Lutreolina crassicaudata*)
Southern opossum (*Didelphis
    marsupialis*)
Virginia or Common opossum
    (*D. virginiana*)
Water opossum or yapok
    (*Chironectes minimus*)
Woolly opossum (e.g. *Caluromys
    lanatus*)

A fox is on the prowl, nose to the ground, following the scent of an animal which could be its next meal. Then it sees its prey, a long-nosed, long-tailed furry creature as big as a cat. It is a Virginia opossum. The fox lunges at the animal and snatches it up in its teeth, shaking it from side to side. The opossum hangs limply in its jaws, eyes closed and tongue hanging out. The fox tosses the opossum to the ground where it lies motionless, as if dead. The fox isn't very interested in dead meat and moves off in search of live prey. As soon as the fox has gone, the "dead" opossum runs away.

"Playing possum", or appearing to be dead, is one way the Virginia opossum escapes the attention of predators. The Virginia opossum is the only one to do this and the only opossum to be found in North America. The many other species of opossum are found from Mexico throughout Central and South America.

Opossums belong to the order of animals known as marsupials. They are mammals which usually raise their young in pouches. Most marsupials live in Australia, including the kangaroo and the koala. Opossums are the only marsupials found outside Australasia.

EXPERT CLIMBERS
Many species of opossum spend much of their life in the trees, and their bodies are well adapted for climbing. Their feet have sharp claws and the big toe on the hind foot is "opposable". This means it can act opposite the other four toes to make grasping easier.

Most opossums also use their long, prehensile tail as an extra limb for grasping. An opossum can curl its tail around a branch to help steady itself or hang upside-down.

The woolly and four-eyed opossums inhabit the humid tropical rain forests of South America. The Woolly opossum has the large, bulging eyes of a typical tree dweller. It usually stays in the upper canopy of the forest, feeding on nectar and fruit.

Four-eyed opossums are usually found in the lower branches of the

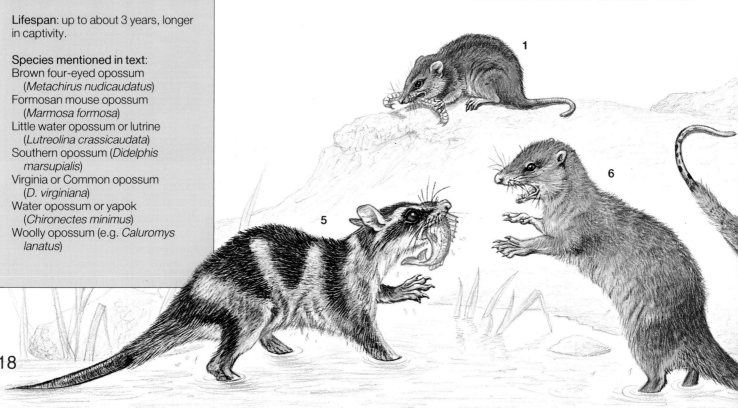

forest or on the ground. There they feed on insects, worms, other animals and fruit. They get their name from the white spots on their forehead. The Brown four-eyed opossum is sometimes called the rat-tailed opossum,

►**Species of opossum and relatives**
Red-sided short-tailed opossum (*Mono-delphis brevicaudata*) eating a centipede **(1)**. Brown four-eyed opossum grooming **(2)**. White-eared opossum (*Didelphis al-biventris*) hanging by its tail **(3)**. Ashby mouse opossum (*Marmosa cinerea*) climbing **(4)**. Yapok catching fish **(5)**. Lutrine being aggressive **(6)**. Woolly opossum **(7)**. Patagonian opossum (*Lestodelphys halli*) hunting a spider **(8)**. Grey four-eyed opossum (*Philander opossum*) eating fruit **(9)**. Black-shouldered opossum (*Caluromysiops irrupta*) eating nut **(10)**. Bushy-tailed opossum (*Glironia venusta*) climbing **(11)**. Opossum relatives: Monito del monte (*Dromiciops australis*) in nest **(12)** and Shrew opossum (*Lestoros inca*) feeding **(13)**.

19

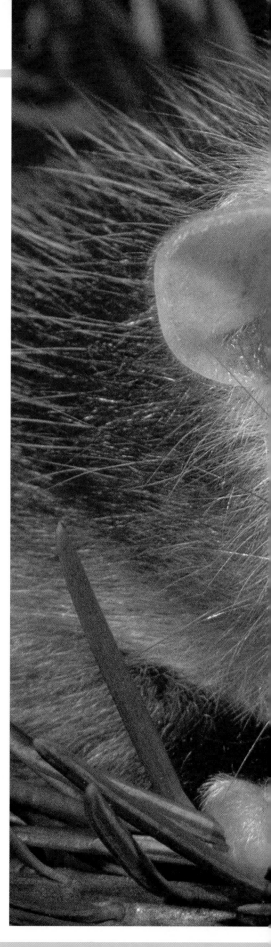

and it does look very much like a rat.

The most numerous of opossum species are the mouse opossums, of which there are nearly 50. They are so called because of their size. Some live in forests, others in more open country and grassland.

The even smaller short-tailed opossums are also found in more open countryside. These mainly ground dwellers look much like shrews.

"WATER WEASELS"

Two species of opossum are good swimmers. One is the Little water opossum or lutrine. Like the weasel, which it resembles, it is a fierce carnivore, feeding on small mammals, birds and frogs. It is found along rivers in open country and even in suburban areas.

The Water opossum or yapok is even better adapted to life in the water. It has webbed feet, and the female can close its pouch under water to protect the young inside. It too is carnivorous.

IN THE POUCH

The female opossum gives birth about 2 weeks after mating. The young are

▲Virginia opossum mother and young. They are about 3 months old and still hitch a ride on their mother.

▶An alert Southern opossum sniffs the air. Its ears move to catch the faintest sounds that may tell it that a juicy meal is near by.

poorly developed, and no bigger than a honeybee. Blind and naked, they claw their way from the birth canal into the mother's furry pouch. There, if they are lucky, they attach themselves to a nipple and start to feed. They remain in the pouch for about 2 months and then start crawling on the mother's back.

The female opossum often produces more offspring than she has nipples. This means that some of the young die. The Virginia opossum has been known to produce over 50 offspring but has only about 13 nipples.

Some opossums, including the mouse and short-tailed opossums, have no pouch for breeding. The young attach themselves to the mother's nipples and dangle from them when she moves. If they fall off they let out a high-pitched cry, calling the mother back.

WOMBATS

On a small wooded island between Australia and Tasmania a scientist settles down to study the creatures of the night. For a while everything is quiet, then the silence is broken by a rustling, shuffling sound. From a hole in a nearby earth bank appears a powerful chunky animal. It is a wombat, another of Australia's unusual pouched mammals.

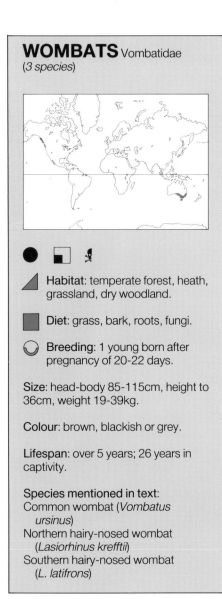

WOMBATS Vombatidae
(*3 species*)

Habitat: temperate forest, heath, grassland, dry woodland.

Diet: grass, bark, roots, fungi.

Breeding: 1 young born after pregnancy of 20-22 days.

Size: head-body 85-115cm, height to 36cm, weight 19-39kg.

Colour: brown, blackish or grey.

Lifespan: over 5 years; 26 years in captivity.

Species mentioned in text:
Common wombat (*Vombatus ursinus*)
Northern hairy-nosed wombat (*Lasiorhinus krefftii*)
Southern hairy-nosed wombat (*L. latifrons*)

◀Part of a wombat warren. In places the Common wombat is classed as a pest because it damages farmers' rabbit-proof fences.

▼To suit its burrowing lifestyle, the pouch of the female wombat opens towards the rear. The cub stays in the pouch until it is 6 to 7 months old.

The wombat is a perfectly designed earth-moving machine – nature's answer to the bulldozer. It is about a metre long, with a heavy, thickset body and a short broad head. Its legs are short and powerful, and its feet are equipped with massive strong claws for digging.

Each animal lives in a maze of tunnels (a warren) up to 30m in length, with several exits, side tunnels and resting chambers. Sometimes, neighbouring warrens may overlap or even interconnect with each other, but the animals keep to themselves and lead mainly solitary lives except in the mating season.

WHO LIVES WHERE
There are three different species of wombat. The most widespread is the Common wombat, which lives in the eucalyptus woodlands of eastern and south-eastern Australia. The other two, called Hairy-nosed wombats, live in much drier parts, where food is even harder to find. The Southern hairy-nosed wombat inhabits dry salt-bush, scrub and savannah woodlands in south-central Australia and is still fairly common. Sadly, the Northern species is now very rare. Only about 20 animals are left, living in one small colony in the dry woodland of eastern Queensland.

SAVING VITAL ENERGY
Wombats live in areas where summer temperatures are high, where food is often scarce, and where there is very little drinking water. Understandably, their whole lifestyle is designed to avoid wasting precious energy and moisture. Most of the day is spent below ground, resting and keeping cool. To save energy, wombats allow their body temperature to fall and their heartbeat to slow while resting, then raise them again at night when it is time to go out in search of food.

Wombats feed mainly on coarse grass, roots and the bark of trees and shrubs. To cope with this tough woody diet they have a single pair of long front teeth which grow continuously, like those of rats and hamsters. Their digestive system too is designed to make the most of the low-quality food. Everything is digested very slowly, and all the valuable moisture is kept in the body. Hardly any is wasted. Their droppings are dry and they pass only tiny amounts of concentrated urine.

◄Hairy-nosed wombats are seasonal breeders, and usually produce a single cub in spring, when food is most plentiful. In times of drought they usually do not produce young.

▼The Common wombat is not a very aggressive animal. Individuals do fight occasionally, but the bites of the attacker seldom do much harm against the shaggy coat of the defender. The wombat's main natural enemy is the dingo.

KOALA

From October to February the eucalyptus forests of eastern Australia echo with strange night-time calls. Long, harsh, indrawn breaths are followed by bellowing growls. No sooner has one call died away than it is answered by others from different parts of the forest. It is the koala's breeding season, and these are the cries of the male koalas.

KOALA *Phascolarctos cinereus*

■ Diet: eucalyptus leaves, from a small number of preferred species.

○ Breeding: 1 young, in summer, after pregnancy of 34-36 days.

Size: head-body to 85cm male, 75cm female; weight 12kg male; 8kg female. (Animals in northern part of range are considerably smaller.)

Colour: grey to reddish-brown, white on chin, chest, and under forearms.

Lifespan: 13 years, 18 in captivity.

● ■

▲ Habitat: eucalyptus forest up to 600m above sea level.

The koala might look like a teddy bear, but it is not related to the bears at all, and is certainly not as friendly as it looks. It will defend itself fiercely with its sharp claws if attacked.

THE COMPLETE SPECIALIST
The koala is a marsupial, a pouched mammal, and one of the most specialized animals in Australia. It lives only in the eucalyptus forests of the east coast, and it eats hardly anything but eucalyptus leaves. Not only that, but with 350 eucalyptus species to choose from, the koala feeds mainly on just 5 or 6. It is a low-quality diet, not very

▼ Even the koala's liver is special. It deals with the poisonous chemicals that occur in some eucalyptus leaves it eats.

rich in energy, so the koala is not very active. It spends almost its entire life in the trees, sleeping for up to 18 hours a day and spending the rest of its time eating. Young leaves are bitten off, then ground to a paste with the large cheek teeth. An adult koala weighing about 9kg will munch its way through up to 1kg of leaves in a day. The animal's intestine is long, to help it digest this mass of leaves.

RAISING A BABY
For most of the year koalas live alone. Their feeding areas may overlap, but the animals do not mix very much, even when there are several of them in a small area of forest. In the breeding season, each breeding male (usually over 4 years old) has several mates. His territory overlaps theirs, and throughout the mating season he is on the move, visiting his mates, calling and bellowing, and chasing rival males from his territory.

In midsummer the female produces a single baby, and like all marsupials it crawls straight into the pouch. There it stays for about 6 months until it is fully developed and ready to cope with the outside world.

The weaning process that follows is very unusual. At first, the baby koala is fed on partly digested leaf pulp

that has already passed through the mother's body. This processed food is easy to digest, but it has another important function. Along with the pulp, the young koala receives a supply of microbes from the mother's gut. These are helpful "bugs" that remain in the youngster's body and enable it to digest tough eucalyptus leaves for itself.

▶ ▼ Once it has left the pouch, a young koala rides about on its mother's back for another 4 to 5 months. The adult is a good climber. It can grasp thin branches with an unusual grip – two fingers at one side of the branch, three at the other.

HONEY POSSUM

As the Moon shines down on a patch of woodland in south-west Australia, a small shrew-like animal scrambles about among the enormous flower-heads of a *Banksia* tree. It is a Honey possum, and it has a special kind of partnership with the tree. As it takes its meal of sweet nectar and clambers over the slenderest of branches, the possum helps the tree by carrying its pollen from flower to flower.

▲The Honey possum's tail is longer than its head and body added together. The animal often uses it like an extra hand.

▼After a few minutes feeding, this Honey possum's face is dusted with the bright yellow pollen of a *Banksia* flower.

HONEY POSSUM
Tarsipes rostratus

● ◼

◣ Habitat: heath, shrubland and open woodland with under-growth.

◼ Diet: nectar and pollen.

◯ Breeding: mainly in early summer. Litters of 2-4 born after pregnancy of about 28 days.

Size: head-body 6.5-9.0cm, tail 7-10cm; weight, male 7-11g, female 8-16g.

Colour: grey-brown above, pale cream below, with three stripes down back.

Lifespan: 1-2 years.

The Honey possum is found only in the heaths, shrublands and open woodlands of south-western Australia. Its name is rather misleading for it does not eat honey at all, but it certainly does like sweet food. It feeds mainly on nectar, and its body is highly specialized for this unusual way of life.

SPECIAL EQUIPMENT

The Honey possum has a long pointed snout for reaching deep inside the flowers it feeds on, and its tongue has a brush-like tip for lapping up the sugary nectar. It can run swiftly through the dense undergrowth, but it is also an expert climber. Its front and back feet are both designed for grasping, just like tiny hands, and this enables the animal to clamber about in the bushes, high among the thinnest twigs and flower stems. It can even grip with its tail, and often hangs upside-down by this extra "arm".

HITCH-HIKING POSSUMS

Honey possums are ready to mate when they are about 6 months old. There is no real courtship period. A male will simply follow a female until she is ready to mate, and once they have mated, the male goes off into the bush. Raising the family is left entirely to the female.

The baby possums are tiny when they are born, and they make their way at once into the mother's deep pouch. There they remain for 8 more weeks, feeding on milk from the four teats inside the pouch. By the time they are ready to leave the pouch for the first time, their eyes are open and they have a warm covering of fur. The whole breeding process is timed so that each litter is ready to leave the pouch when food is most plentiful, in autumn, spring or early summer.

At first the young are left in an old bird's nest or hollow tree while the mother feeds, but after a few days they climb on to her back and hitch a ride, although they soon become too heavy for her. At about 11 weeks they stop taking milk from the mother, and soon after this they set off to find a home of their own.

A PLACE TO LIVE

Outside the breeding season, Honey possums spend most of their time in separate home territories about one-and-a-half times the size of a soccer field. The territories overlap at the edges, but the animals seldom seem to fight with one another. However, things are different in the breeding season. Females with young spend their time in much smaller territories.

These are strictly private, and strangers, especially males, are very quickly and aggressively chased away.

At present, survival of the Honey possum is not threatened. But being an animal that is found only in one small part of the world, it is likely quickly to become endangered as much of its habitat is destroyed. In the future it may be necessary to set up special reserves to protect this unusual little marsupial.

▼ Honey possums are active mainly at night, and they rely on their sense of smell as well as their large eyes to find their food and to locate other animals.

POSSUMS AND GLIDERS

POSSUMS AND GLIDERS Pseudocheiridae, Burramyidae, Petauridae (*30 species*)

● ■ 🐾

◢ **Habitat:** forest, scrub, heath.

◥ **Diet:** leaves, gum, nectar insects.

○ **Breeding:** 1 or 2 (ringtail possums) or 4-6 (pygmy possums) young after pregnancy of 2-4 weeks.

Size: smallest (Little pygmy possum): head-body 6.4cm, tail 7.1cm, weight 7g; largest (Rock ringtail possum): up to head-body 38cm, tail 27cm, weight 2kg.

Colour: grey or brown coat, paler underneath, often darker eye patches.

Lifespan: up to 15 years.

Species mentioned in text:
Common ringtail possum
  (*Pseudocheirus peregrinus*)
Feathertail or Pygmy glider (*Acrobates pygmaeus*)
Greater glider (*Petauroides volans*)
Striped possum (*Dactylopsila trivirgata*)
Sugar glider (*Petaurus breviceps*)
Yellow-bellied or Fluffy glider
  (*P. australis*)

High in the eucalypt forest a long-tailed animal leaps from a branch into the air. It is not aiming for another branch nearby but for a tree trunk over 30m away. As it becomes airborne it spreads its arms and legs wide, stretching out a flap of skin between wrists and ankles. Gracefully and effortlessly the animal glides and manoeuvres through the trees to make a perfect landing, right on target.

▲The Feathertail glider of eastern Australia is one of the several species of pygmy possums.

►The Sugar glider (**1**) and Yellow-bellied glider (**2**) are both expert gliders. They feed on sweet sap and gum. The Yellow-bellied glider makes V-shaped notches in the tree trunks when it feeds.

◄A Common ringtail possum curls its tail as it eats its favourite leaves (**1**). The Striped possum eats an insect (**2**).

DICK TWINNEY 94

Animals that glide are common in the forests of Australia, New Guinea and the nearby islands. They include the Yellow-bellied or Fluffy glider of eastern Australia which can "fly" up to l00m. All the Australian and New Guinea gliders belong to three related families: the ringtail possums, the gliders and the pygmy possums.

Australian possums were so named because they looked like the American opossums. Like opossums they are marsupials – after birth, their tiny naked young crawl into the mother's pouch, attach themselves to a nipple and suckle for several weeks.

GLIDING AND GRIPPING
There are nine species that glide, using a membrane of skin between their limbs. When flying, the long tail of a glider stretches out behind. This helps steady the flight and aids steering. Most gliders have a thick furry tail, but the Feathertail glider's tail has tufts of hair on the end which look like the flight feathers of an arrow.

The gliders have long and sharp claws, especially on their forefeet. This helps them grip the bark of the trees when they land. Both gliders and non-gliders have large hands and feet with digits that can be spread apart to get a firm grip.

The non-gliders have a prehensile tail with which they can also grip. The tail is usually naked underneath to get a firmer hold. The ringtail possums have the habit of curling up the end of the tail when they are not using it. This is how they got their name.

VARIED DIETS
The ringtail possums and the closely related Greater glider eat mainly leaves. The Yellow-bellied and Sugar gliders mostly feed on the sap and gum of trees such as wattle and eucalyptus.

The Striped possum eats insects. It has large teeth, a long tongue and a very long fourth finger to help get at insects and larvae beneath tree bark. It is particularly partial to eating ants, bees, termites and other wood-boring insects. As it picks away at the bark, it produces a shower of wood-chips. The mouse-like pygmy possums prefer nectar and pollen. This rich diet makes them breed bigger litters (up to 7) than the other possums and makes them grow more quickly.

KANGAROOS

KANGAROOS Macropodidae and Potoroidae
(60 species)

weight up to 90kg. In larger species, males bigger than females.

Colour: mainly shades of brown or grey; some have contrasting facial markings or stripes on body or tail.

Lifespan: up to 20 years in the wild, 28 years in captivity.

Species mentioned in text:
Eastern grey kangaroo (*Macropus giganteus*)
Lumholtz's tree kangaroo (*Dendrolagus lumholtzi*)
Musky rat kangaroo (*Hypsiprymnodon moschatus*)
Red kangaroo (*Macropus rufus*)
Wallaroo or euro or Hill kangaroo (*M. robustus*)
Western grey kangaroo (*M. fuliginosus*)

○ ■ ☠

◢ **Habitat:** inland plain and semi-desert to tropical rain forest and hills.

■ **Diet:** grasses, other low-growing plants, shoots of bushes.

◎ **Breeding:** 1 joey after pregnancy of 27-36 days, plus a period in the pouch of 5-11 months.

Size: smallest (Musky rat kangaroo): head-body 28cm, plus 14cm tail, weight 0.5kg; largest (Red kangaroo): head-body 1.65m, plus 1.07m tail,

Two grey kangaroos sip water from the edge of a small river. They turn and move slowly up the bank. Suddenly alarmed by a flock of birds landing to drink, they begin to move fast. They thump their back legs down hard and spring into the air. Each bound sends them higher and faster, until they are in full flight, travelling at 50kph in jumps 4m long.

The kangaroo family is large. There are about 50 species. The larger species are called kangaroos, the smaller ones wallabies. There are also 10 small species known as rat kangaroos and bettongs. Kangaroos are marsupials, animals of which the female has a pouch where she keeps the young.

HOW THEY HOP
The whole group have long back legs and travel fast by hopping. The long tail works as a counterbalance to the weight of the body as they jump. When moving slowly, kangaroos may use the front legs and tail as a tripod to

▼▶ **Larger kangaroos and wallabies**
The Bridled nailtail wallaby (*Onychogalea frenata*) (**1**) lives in open country. The wallaroo (**2**) is widely distributed in Australia. The rabbit-sized quokka (*Setonix brachyurus*) lives in West Australia (**3**).The Red-legged pademelon (*Thylogale stigmatica*) (**4**) and the Yellow-footed rock wallaby (*Petrogale xanthopus*) (**5**) are mainly nocturnal. The Grey forest wallaby (*Dorcopsis veterum*) lives in New Guinea (**6**).

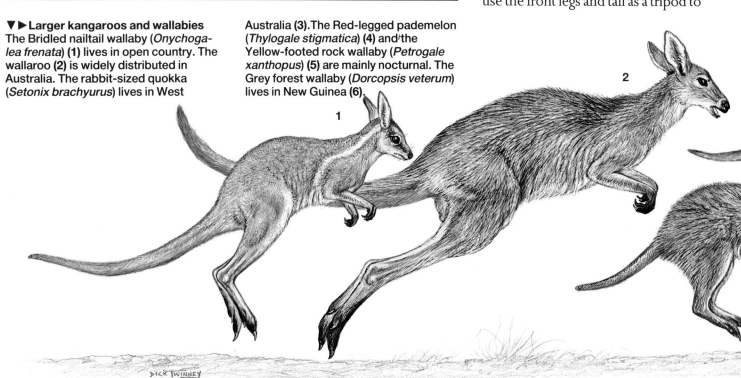

DICK TWINNEY 84

take the weight, then they swing the back legs forward. Next, the back legs support them while they move their front legs and tail.

The long and narrow back foot has four toes. Two of these are large. The other two are small and joined together. They make a kind of comb which a kangaroo uses to keep its fur in good condition.

Kangaroos are plant eaters. They have good chewing teeth in the back of the mouth. As with elephants, their teeth move forwards as they grow older and the front teeth wear down. Kangaroos have large stomachs where there are bacteria which help break down the tough plant food. Most kangaroo species feed at night.

WIDE VARIETY

The big Red kangaroo lives mainly on open plains. It has a thick woolly coat which helps keep out both heat and cold. During the heat of the day it rests in the shade of a bush, feeding when it is cooler. It needs little water, but even in a dry brown landscape it will find newly sprouting grasses and herbs to eat.

▲ Male, female and joey (young in pouch) of the largest marsupial, the Red kangaroo, which lives in grassland.

▼ Kangaroos and wallabies, as plant-eaters, are the Australasian equivalents of African hoofed mammals.

Wallaroos are also desert animals and can exist on even poorer food. The Eastern and Western grey kangaroos live in wooded country. They eat the grasses that grow between trees and they need to drink more often.

Many smaller wallabies like to live in scrub or dense thickets. In some parts of Australia much of this kind of vegetation has been cleared for farms or ranches, and this is one reason why some of the small kangaroos have become rarer. Another reason is that they have suffered from introduced rabbits competing for food and living

▲The back legs of tree kangaroos are fairly short, but the tail is long and provides a good balancing limb.

▼Small- and medium-sized kangaroos The Lesser forest wallaby (*Dorcopsulus macleayi*) **(1)** lives in New Guinea. The Musky rat kangaroo **(2)**. Lumholtz's tree kangaroo **(3)**. The Desert rat kangaroo (*Caloprymnus campestris*) **(4)**. The rare boodie (*Bettongia lesueur*) **(5)** burrows. The Rufous hare wallaby (*Lagorchestes hirsutus*) **(6)**. The Long-nosed potoroo (*Potorous tridactylus*) **(7)** and the Rufous bettong (*Aepyprymnus rufescens*) **(9)** are now rare. The Banded hare wallaby (*Lagostrophus fasciatus*) **(8)** survives only on coastal islands.

places, and also from being hunted by introduced cats and foxes.

Some kangaroos live in hot wet forests, such as are found in northern Australia and New Guinea. Tree kangaroos (such as Lumholtz's tree kangaroo) climb, and have some of the brightest coloured fur among marsupials. They are agile, making big leaps from one tree to another. But on the ground they are rather slow and clumsy.

SOCIAL AND FAMILY LIFE
Many of the smaller kangaroos live alone, but the Red and grey kangaroos live in groups (called "mobs"). From 2 to 10 move around together, but larger numbers may come together where food is good. In the largest species the males may be twice the size of the females. In Red kangaroos and wallaroos the males and females are different colours.

Kangaroos, like other marsupials, have a very short pregnancy, about a month long. Even in the biggest kangaroos, the baby weighs less than 1g at birth. The baby has big arms and small legs. It crawls by itself to the mother's pouch, where it attaches to one of the four teats. Here it suckles and grows. After several months it takes trips outside the pouch. Even when it leaves the pouch completely (up to a year after birth) it suckles for a few months more.

33

ANTEATERS

The Giant anteater lumbering across the dried grassland is heading for one of the anthills dotting the landscape. It can't see the mound because of its poor eyesight, but it can smell the ants. When it reaches the earthy mound, it slashes a hole in it and thrusts in its snout. Flicking its long tongue in and out, it begins to feed on the startled insects.

The Giant anteater is the largest of the anteaters of South and Central America. They all feed almost entirely on ants and termites. They have a tube-like snout and a long narrow tongue covered with a sticky saliva. The Giant anteater can flick its tongue a distance of some 60cm up to 150 times a minute.

The ants stick to the saliva on the tongue and are taken into the mouth.

The mouth opening is surprisingly small – not much bigger across than a pencil. Anteaters have no teeth. They lightly chew their prey using little hard lumps on the roof of the mouth and on the cheeks.

▼The Southern tamandua's gold, brown and white patterned coat gives it good camouflage in the scrubland and forest where it lives.

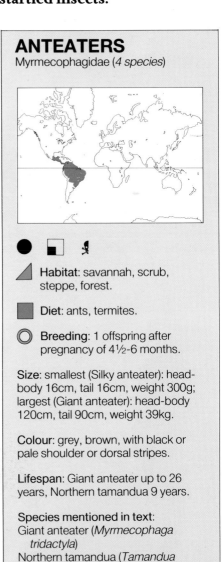

ANTEATERS
Myrmecophagidae (*4 species*)

● ■ ☇

◣ Habitat: savannah, scrub, steppe, forest.

■ Diet: ants, termites.

◎ Breeding: 1 offspring after pregnancy of 4½-6 months.

Size: smallest (Silky anteater): head-body 16cm, tail 16cm, weight 300g; largest (Giant anteater): head-body 120cm, tail 90cm, weight 39kg.

Colour: grey, brown, with black or pale shoulder or dorsal stripes.

Lifespan: Giant anteater up to 26 years, Northern tamandua 9 years.

Species mentioned in text:
Giant anteater (*Myrmecophaga tridactyla*)
Northern tamandua (*Tamandua mexicana*)
Silky anteater (*Cyclopes didactylus*)
Southern tamandua (*Tamandua tetradactyla*)

"STINKERS OF THE FOREST"

The Giant anteater is usually active during the day, but it spends part of the time asleep. The other species of anteaters are mainly nocturnal and spend much of their time in the trees. Unlike their giant relative, they have a prehensile tail which helps them grip the branches when they climb.

The two species of tamandua, the Northern and Southern, are only about half the size of the Giant anteater. They have a striped coat, which gives them their alternative name: Collared anteater. They have also been given the nickname "stinker of the forest" because of the unpleasant smell they sometimes give off.

The much smaller Silky anteater hardly ever comes down from the trees. Its snout is much shorter than that of the other species. It is often called the two-toed anteater because three of its five fingers do not show. It has short silky fur.

POWERFUL CLAWS

All the anteaters have large sharp and powerful curved claws on their forefeet; tamanduas have three, the Giant and Silky anteaters two. They use these claws to open up anthills and termite mounds and also to defend themselves.

When alarmed or attacked, anteaters rise up on their hind legs, using their tail as a prop to steady themselves. As their attacker gets closer, they slash at it with their claws, which on the Giant anteater are up to 10cm long. Another powerful weapon is a crushing bear-hug, delivered with their strong forelimbs.

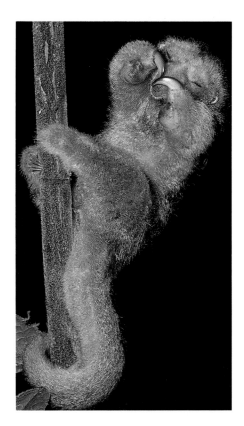

▶On the defensive, a Silky anteater covers its face with its claws, while clinging to a branch with feet and tail.

▼A young Giant anteater rides piggyback on its mother. Both are identical in colour, making the young one rather difficult to see.

ARMADILLOS

It is late evening in the heart of Florida's swampland. Coming to a stream, an armadillo stops as if wondering what to do next. Then it steps into the water and disappears beneath the surface. Holding its breath, it walks along the bottom of the stream. More than five minutes pass before it reappears on the other side and continues on its way. Had the stream been any wider, the armadillo would have swum across, swallowing air to make it float better.

▼Southern three-banded armadillo (1), pichi (2) and Lesser fairy armadillo (3).

There are 20 species of armadillo in the Americas, ranging from Oklahoma in the north to Argentina in the south. Most widespread is the Common long-nosed armadillo, also called the Nine-banded armadillo, found in the United States.

The Spanish word *armadillo* means "little armoured one". This is a very good description of an animal that is covered with a number of hard bony plates, called scutes. Broad shield-like plates usually cover the shoulders and rear of the body. In the middle are a varying number of circular bands, which flex as the animal moves. The head, tail and limbs are also protected by armour. The underside of the body is covered only by hairy skin, but an attacker is rarely able to reach this weak-spot.

GREAT DIGGERS

Armadillos have short but powerful limbs, tipped with strong claws. The animals use their claws when digging for insect prey or making a burrow to sleep in. The Common long-nosed armadillo is an especially efficient digger. When it smells insects or other small prey in the soil, it digs frantically for them, keeping its long nose pressed to the ground. It holds its breath while digging, to stop itself inhaling the dirt.

The burrows armadillos dig can be as much as 2m underground and have two or more entrances. They contain one or two nest chambers lined with grass and other plant material. An armadillo may dig 10 or more such burrows, which it uses on different days in no fixed pattern.

1

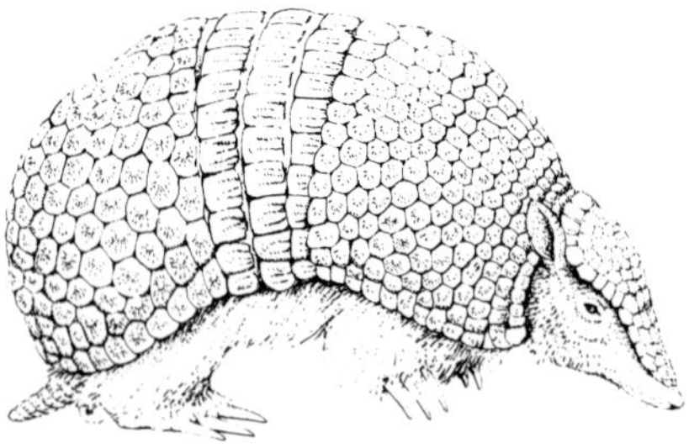

2

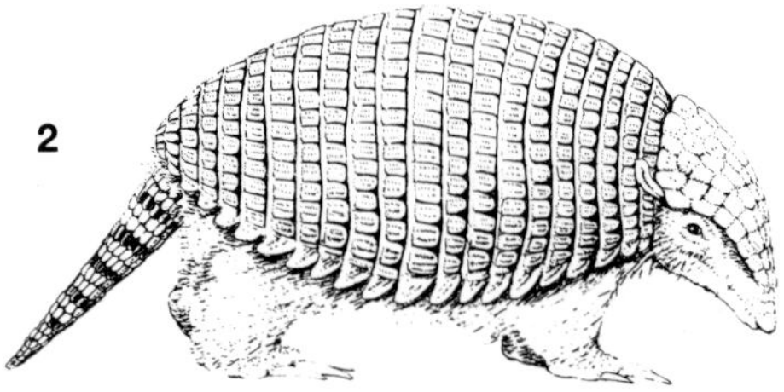

3

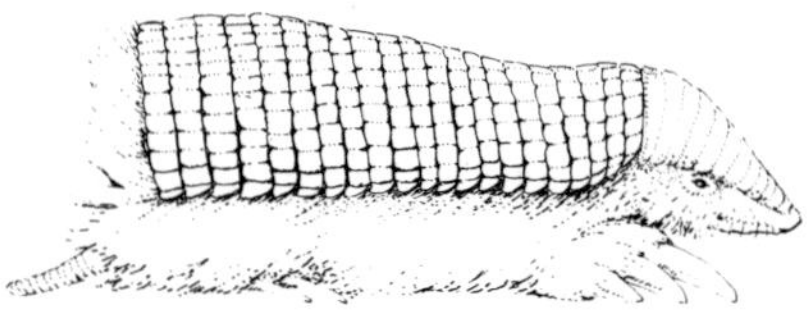

ARMADILLOS

Dasypodidae (*20 species*)

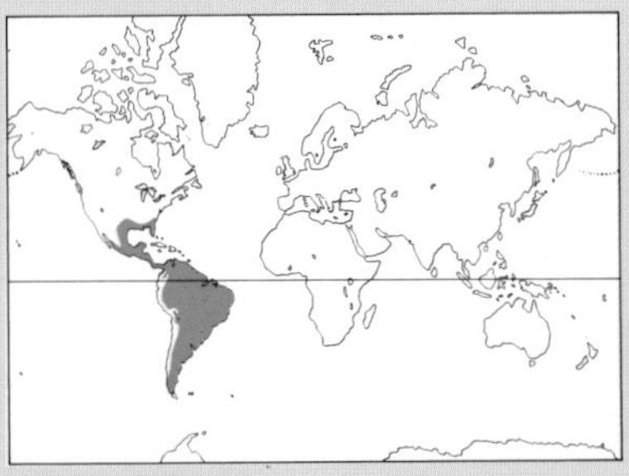

Habitat: wide range, desert, savannah, scrub, forest.

Diet: insects, especially ants and termites, other small animals.

Breeding: number of offspring varies, 1 (fairy and three-banded armadillos), 4 (most long-nosed armadillos), 12 (Southern lesser long-nosed armadillo). Pregnancy usually 60-65 days.

Size: smallest (Lesser fairy armadillo): head-body 12.5cm, tail 2.5cm, weight 80g; largest (Giant armadillo): head-body 100cm, tail 45cm, weight 60kg.

Colour: pinkish or yellowish dark brown armour, pale or dark brown hairs between plates and on underside skin.

Lifespan: up to 15 years.

Species mentioned in text:
- Brazilian lesser long-nosed armadillo (*Dasypus septemcinctus*)
- Common long-nosed or Nine-banded armadillo (*D. novemcinctus*)
- Giant armadillo (*Priodontes maximus*)
- Larger hairy armadillo (*Chaetophractus villosus*)
- Lesser fairy or Pink fairy armadillo (*Chlamyphorus truncatus*)
- Pichi (*Zaedyus pichiy*)
- Southern lesser long-nosed armadillo (*Dasypus hybridus*)
- Southern three-banded armadillo (*Tolypeutes matacus*)

GIANTS AND FAIRIES

Armadillos spend most of their lives alone. They mark their home territory with their urine and droppings and with a yellowish smelly liquid given off by glands at their rear. When armadillos do cross into each other's territory, they may fight, with much kicking, chasing, and squealing.

When an armadillo is being hunted by a predator it may dig itself out of trouble and disappear beneath the soil. Or it may simply crouch low on the ground so that only its armour shows. Three-banded armadillos can roll themselves completely into a ball, safe even from jaguars.

There is a great difference in size among armadillos. Largest of the family is the increasingly rare Giant armadillo which measures up to 150cm from head to tail. The smallest is only one-tenth this length. This is the almost shrimp-like Lesser fairy armadillo, also called the Pink fairy armadillo, which has a dense coat of white hair on its sides and under-parts. The Lesser fairy spends much of its life tunnelling underground – something its giant relative could never do.

▲Like all the armadillos, this Larger hairy armadillo has large strong claws for digging. It can take a variety of foods, including maggots from inside the rotting carcasses of other animals. It sometimes burrows deep within a carcass.

▼The Brazilian lesser long-nosed armadillo digs a shallow burrow to rest in during the day. Like all the other armadillos it is classed as an *Edentate* (without teeth) but has a set of up to 100 primitive teeth.

SLOTHS

Tree-fellers in a Central American rain forest stop their destruction to watch a strange animal move through the near-by tree canopy. It is a sloth. The animal can barely walk, and mostly hangs upside down in trees. It travels no more than about 40m a day going at full speed. But in the forest it can find a supply of food all year round.

The five species of sloth are split into two families according to the number of claws on their front feet. As the name suggests, the three-toed sloths have three claws, while the two-toed sloths have just two. They all have three claws on their back paws.

These strong, curved, 10cm-long hooks help the sloth climb easily among the branches. But on the ground the animal is almost helpless and can only manage a clumsy crawl. Surprisingly, sloths are very good swimmers, although they rarely leave the safety of the trees.

PORTABLE CAMOUFLAGE

The sloth's long, thick, shaggy hair is greyish-brown in colour, but the animal usually has a greenish tinge. The colour comes from algae (microscopic plants) that grow in tiny grooves on each hair. This portable plant-life helps camouflage the sloth as it moves among the branches. Because of its upside-down life-style, the sloth's hair grows in the opposite direction to that of most animals. It grows from the belly towards the back so that rain-water runs off easily.

The sloth's colouring, slow motion and very unusual position hanging beneath the branches all help keep it safe, even in a habitat full of fierce predators.

WHO NEEDS ENERGY?

Sloths live entirely on leaves, which they grind to a pulp with their large cheek teeth. They have no front teeth. It is a low-energy diet, but the sloth needs little fuel. It uses energy at only half the rate of most mammals of similar size.

To conserve energy it lets its body temperature drop during the cooler

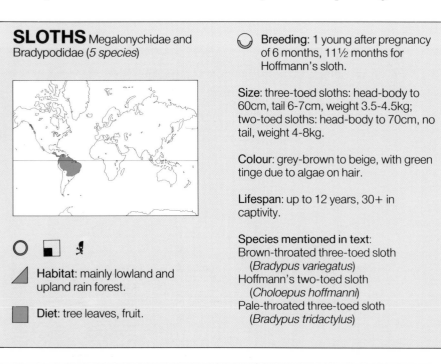

SLOTHS Megalonychidae and Bradypodidae (*5 species*)

○ **Breeding:** 1 young after pregnancy of 6 months, 11½ months for Hoffmann's sloth.

Size: three-toed sloths: head-body to 60cm, tail 6-7cm, weight 3.5-4.5kg; two-toed sloths: head-body to 70cm, no tail, weight 4-8kg.

Colour: grey-brown to beige, with green tinge due to algae on hair.

Lifespan: up to 12 years, 30+ in captivity.

Species mentioned in text:
Brown-throated three-toed sloth
  (*Bradypus variegatus*)
Hoffmann's two-toed sloth
  (*Choloepus hoffmanni*)
Pale-throated three-toed sloth
  (*Bradypus tridactylus*)

○ ■ ☠

△ **Habitat:** mainly lowland and upland rain forest.

■ **Diet:** tree leaves, fruit.

◄After 6-9 months this young Brown-throated three-toed sloth will inherit part of its mother's feeding area and also her preference for the leaves of certain tree species.

▼Hoffmann's two-toed sloth in the rain forest of Panama.

hours of night and when resting. To warm up again it simply moves out into a patch of strong sunlight.

LIVING HAMMOCK

Adult sloths are solitary for most of the year. Breeding males advertise their presence by marking tree branches with a powerful scent produced by their anal glands.

Most sloths breed at any time of the year. The exception seems to be the Pale-throated three-toed sloth of Guyana, which breeds only after the rainy season. A single baby is born in all species and is cradled on the mother's belly, where it will remain for up to 9 months. It feeds on milk for only about 1 month and from then on feeds on the leaves it can reach from its mobile hammock.

SHREWS

Ever since it was born a year ago, the little shrew scurrying through the leaf litter has been on the go. Every hour or so it has had to eat to give it the energy for its very active way of life. Now it is in trouble. Its one set of teeth has worn down almost to nothing. It can hardly chew even the softest prey. Suddenly the scurrying stops. The shrew drops in its tracks, dead of starvation.

As a zoological family, shrews are by far the most successful of the insect-eaters or insectivores. Out of the 345 species of insectivores, 246 are shrews. They are found throughout North and Central America, Europe, Asia and most of Africa. Among the 246 species there are over 20 distinct types or genera.

Some species can be found widely, others only in certain areas. The Eurasian water shrew is found throughout Northern Europe and Asia; the Sri Lanka shrew, only on that island.

SQUEALS AND ECHOES

All the shrews are broadly similar in appearance. They have a greyish or brownish soft-furred body and a tail.

SHREWS Soricidae
(246 species)

Size: smallest (Pygmy white-toothed shrew): head-tail 3.5cm, weight 2g; largest (African forest shrew): head-tail 29cm, weight 35g.

Colour: brown, grey.

Lifespan: up to 18 months.

Species mentioned in text:
American short-tailed shrew (*Blarina brevicauda*)
Armoured shrew (*Scutisorex somereni*)
European or Eurasian water shrew (*Neomys fodiens*)
Pygmy white-toothed shrew (*Suncus etruscus*)
Sri Lanka shrew (*Podihik kura*)
Tibetan water shrew (*Nectogale elegans*)

○ ■

Habitat: wide range, from desert and grassland to forest.

Diet: worms, insects and other small animals, sometimes seeds and nuts.

○ **Breeding:** up to 10 offspring after pregnancy of 2-3 weeks.

They look at first sight like a mouse, but have a much more pointed nose. Their eyes and ears are small and often nearly hidden by their fur. Their sight is poor, but their hearing is good.

Shrews spend most of their time alone. They squeal and twitter when they come across other shrews wandering into their territory. Some use sonar (echo-location) to find their way around. They make high-pitched clicking noises and then listen for the echoes from obstacles in their path.

▼This shrew seems to have bitten off more than it can chew. But large juicy earthworms are one of its favourite foods, and it is quite able to cope. Shrews need to eat every few hours to stay alive. They often eat more than their own body weight every day.

The water shrews are well adapted for their life in the water. Stiff hairs fringe their feet and tail, helping them swim better. The Tibetan water shrew even has webbed feet.

The Armoured shrew of Central Africa boasts the most unusual feature among shrews. It has enlarged vertebrae on the backbone, which have tough spines attached. It is said that they can support the weight of a man lying on top.

▲The Pygmy white-toothed shrew is the smallest land mammal on Earth, measuring just 35mm long and weighing 2g. It lives in African scrub and savannah.

▼A mother gives young shrews a guided tour of their territory. Each animal grips the rump of the one in front, so none gets lost on the journey.

FIERCE FIGHTERS

The only time one usually sees shrews is when they have dropped dead in the open. When they are alive, shrews are secretive creatures that stay out of sight among the leaf litter if there is a disturbance near by. Dead shrews often remain uneaten for a long time because of the evil-smelling scent that comes from glands in their body. Many predators leave them alone for the same reason.

Some shrews have not only glands like this, but also poisonous saliva. The American short-tailed shrew and some water shrews have venomous bites that help them attack quite large animals such as mice, frogs and fish. For their size, shrews are among the fiercest animals in the world.

Several species of shrew are known to nibble and lick their rectum as soon as their intestines are free of droppings. They probably do this to obtain minerals and vitamins from partly digested food and droplets of fat in the rectum.

◄A European water shrew dives into a stream for food. It will feed on small fish, crustaceans and small frogs. Note the silvery air bubbles clinging to its fur.

MOLES AND DESMANS

A metre under the ground a female mole suckles her five young. Soon she leaves them in the nest chamber and climbs up the sloping passage to her feeding grounds. There the tunnels are just beneath the surface and act as pitfall traps for the insect larvae and worms on which she feeds. But her catch is not enough to satisfy her, so she digs a fresh tunnel in search of richer pickings before returning to feed her family.

▼A European mole emerges from the middle of a molehill. Its powerful fore-limbs are spade-like and tipped with strong claws.

MOLES AND DESMANS Talpidae and Chrysochloridae (*47 species*)

○ ◨ 🐾

Habitat: moles: mostly sub-terranean, but from desert (golden moles) to grassland and forest; desmans: lakes and rivers.

Diet: moles: worms, insects, slugs, snails, spiders, lizards; desmans: water insects, crustaceans, and sometimes fish.

◎ **Breeding:** up to 7 offspring after pregnancy of 1 month (European mole).

Size: smallest (shrew moles): head-body 2.4cm, tail 2.4cm, weight 10g; largest (Russian desman) head-body 21cm, tail 21cm, weight 550g.

Colour: grey, brownish-black; golden moles: reddish-brown, golden.

Lifespan: 3-5 years.

Species mentioned in text:
European mole (*Talpa europaea*)
Grant's desert golden mole (*Eremitalpa granti*)
Pyrenean desman (*Galemys pyrenaicus*)
Russian desman (*Desmana moschata*)
Star-nosed mole (*Condylura cristata*)

The European mole spends most of its life underground, and its body is well suited to this life. It has a rounded body covered in thick velvety fur. Its most noticeable feature is its huge forelimbs, with which it burrows through the soil.

When digging, the mole first braces itself with its back legs. Then it moves its forelimbs forwards into the soil and then sideways and backwards in almost a swimming motion. From time to time it digs a shaft upwards and pushes the loose soil it has excavated to the surface. This results in the familiar molehill.

BLIND AS A MOLE

Moles are very active creatures and eat frequently. The European mole spends about four hours eating followed by four hours resting, day and night for much of the year. On occasions it may burrow nearly 100m a day if food is scarce.

Moles have very small eyes, almost hidden by their fur, and they are all but blind. For a life underground this does not matter. Their main sense is that of touch. They have sensitive whiskers on the snout and also sensitive little bumps there.

Moles' sense of smell is also good.

They smear their burrows with scent to warn other moles away. Moles have some sense of hearing, although their ears are little more than fur-covered holes.

RIVER AND DESERT MOLES

Some moles are excellent swimmers. The Star-nosed mole lives in tunnels in river banks and swims a lot. The desmans, the largest of the moles, are even more aquatic. They have webbed feet, a flat paddle-like tail and a trumpet-like snout which they use like a snorkel. One species lives in Russia, the other in the Pyrenees mountains. Both are now scarce.

None of the moles mentioned so far are found in Africa. On that continent the moles are represented by 18 species of the almost tail-less golden moles. The name "golden" is taken from the greyish-yellow coat of Grant's desert golden mole, which lives in South-west Africa.

▲The Star-nosed mole (1) is equally at home on land or in the water. The Pyrenean desman (2) spends nearly all its time in the water.

▼This Star-nosed mole has caught a worm. It has 22 fleshy tentacles on the end of its nose.

ELEPHANT-SHREWS

ELEPHANT-SHREWS
Macroscelididae (*15 species*)

Habitat: from forest to desert.

Diet: insects, spiders, worms.

Breeding: usually 1 or 2 offspring after pregnancy of 40-65 days.

Size: smallest (Short-eared elephant-shrew): from head-body 10.4cm, tail 11.5cm, weight 45g; largest (Golden-rumped elephant-shrew): up to head-body 29cm, tail 25cm, weight 540g.

Colour: grey, light or dark brown coat, with streaks or patches.

Lifespan: up to 4 years.

Species mentioned in text:
Black and rufous elephant-shrew
(*Rhynchocyon petersi*)
Golden-rumped elephant-shrew
(*R. chrysopygus*)
Rufous elephant-shrew (*Elephantulus rufescens*)
Short-eared elephant-shrew
(*Macroscelides proboscideus*)

From its perch, the eagle spots the eye-catching rear of the Golden-rumped elephant-shrew some distance away. It turns its head and shuffles its legs, preparing to attack. But the elephant-shrew has seen the eagle move and knows it has enough time to escape. It slaps the ground noisily with its tail as if to say, "I've seen you. You can't catch me!"

The elephant-shrews are insect-eating mammals that live in most parts of Africa except the west. They have a long snout like an elephant's trunk and a similar diet to shrews – hence their name. But they are quite unrelated to shrews (or elephants!). They are much bigger, with big ears, large bulging eyes and very long legs, almost like a miniature antelope.

There are two main groups of elephant-shrews: giant ones, such as the Golden-rumped elephant-shrew, and small ones, such as the Rufous and Short-eared elephant-shrews. The small ones are approximately mouse-sized, the large ones bigger than rats.

▼**Four species of elephant-shrews**
North African elephant-shrew (*Elephantulus rozeti*) washing its face (**1**). Short-eared elephant-shrew clearing a trail (**2**). Four-toed elephant-shrew (*Petrodamus tetradactylus*) probing for insects with its tongue (**3**). Chequered elephant-shrew (*Rhynchocyon cirnei*) scent-marking with its tail glands (**4**).

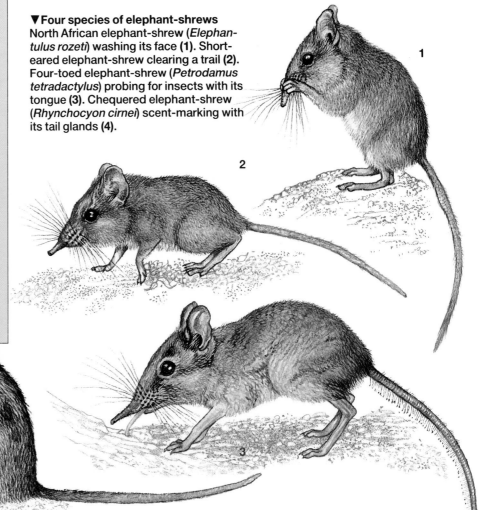

TAKING FLIGHT

The elephant-shrew's long legs make it a very fast mover. If the Golden-rumped elephant-shrew wants to escape from predators, it does so in leaps and bounds at speeds of 25kph.

Some of the smaller species, including the Rufous elephant-shrew, make trails through their territory. They keep these trails free from debris so that they can when necessary run along them at top speed. It could make the difference between life and death if they were chased.

KEEPING IN TOUCH

Elephant-shrews generally live in mating pairs. Both sexes are similar in

▼A Rufous elephant-shrew forages for insects (1). It lives for only about 2½ years in the wild. The giant Black and rufous elephant-shrew devours a centipede, one of its favourite foods (2).

▲The conspicuous patch on the Golden-rumped elephant-shrew could be a target for attackers. But the animal has a good chance of surviving these attacks because the skin is very thick there.

appearance, and share the work of maintaining their trails. They also both defend their territory against intruders. The males fight off rival males, the females fight rival females.

The pair do not spend all their time together, but they keep in contact around their home territory. They may do so by scent-marking, by slapping on the ground with their tail or by drumming with their hind feet.

Young elephant-shrews are born very well developed, with a furry coat and sometimes with their eyes already open. They are usually able to leave the nest with their mother in a day or so. In parts of Kenya especially, many fall victim to hunters, who snare and eat them. The forest-dwelling giant elephant-shrews are threatened by destruction of their homes.

COLUGOS

As dusk falls in a Malayan coconut plantation a colugo leaves the tree-hole in which it spent the day asleep. Gripping the trunk with needle-sharp claws, it climbs to the top, then launches itself into space. It glides through the trees to land on a trunk over 100m away.

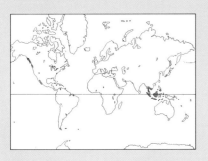

COLUGOS Cynocephalidae
(*2 species*)

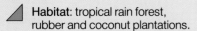

● ■

◢ Habitat: tropical rain forest, rubber and coconut plantations.

■ Diet: leaves, shoots, buds and flowers; some soft fruits.

◡ Breeding: 1 young (rarely 2) after pregnancy of 60 days.

Size: Malayan colugo: head-body 34-42cm, tail 22-27cm, "wingspan" 70cm, weight 1.0-1.8kg. Philippine colugo: head-body 33-38cm, tail 22-27cm, weight 1.0-1.5kg.

Colour: back, mottled grey-brown with white spots; paler underneath. Philippine species darker.

Lifespan: not known.

Species mentioned in text:
Malayan colugo (*Cynocephalus variegatus*)
Philippine colugo (*C. volans*)

▶The dappled grey and brown colouring of the Malayan colugo provides a very effective camouflage against tree bark.

The two species of colugo of Southeast Asia puzzled scientists for many years. Some thought they were lemurs – the animals are often called "flying lemurs" – others grouped them with the bats or the insect-eaters. Now we know they are none of these things. They are the only survivors of an ancient and very specialized group of animals, and they even have their own group name Dermoptera, which means skin-wing.

NATURE'S HANG-GLIDERS

It is dark inside a tropical rain forest. Tall straight tree trunks tower 30m or more above the ground. Most of the food is up there too, high in the leafy canopy. Birds and bats get to the food by flying. Squirrrels, cats and monkeys reach it by climbing. But a colugo scrambles up there then glides from tree to tree.

Tough, flexible flaps of skin stretch from the sides of a colugo's neck to the tips of its fingers and toes, and to the end of its tail. At rest, the skin hangs around the animal like a loose cloak, but when it leaps from a tree and stretches out its legs, the skin is pulled tight into a perfect kite shape.

With slight movements of its body a colugo can steer its chosen path through the air. One glide measured by scientists carried a colugo 136m to a landing point only 12m lower than its take-off point.

FOREST HIGH-LIFE

Colugos are so specialized for life in the trees that they can hardly move if placed on the ground. They climb with the aid of sharp claws, reaching up to grip a tree trunk with their front paws, then bringing up both back feet together.

Both species spend the daylight hours at rest in a tree-hole or clinging to a tree trunk. In plantations they may curl up in the middle of a palm frond. At dusk they emerge to feed on the forest vegetation, pulling small branches within reach, then stripping off the leaves with their strong tongue and sharp teeth. Colugos move through the forest as they feed, and will use favourite gliding trees again and again. Where the feeding areas of several colugos overlap, they often share particularly good take-off trees.

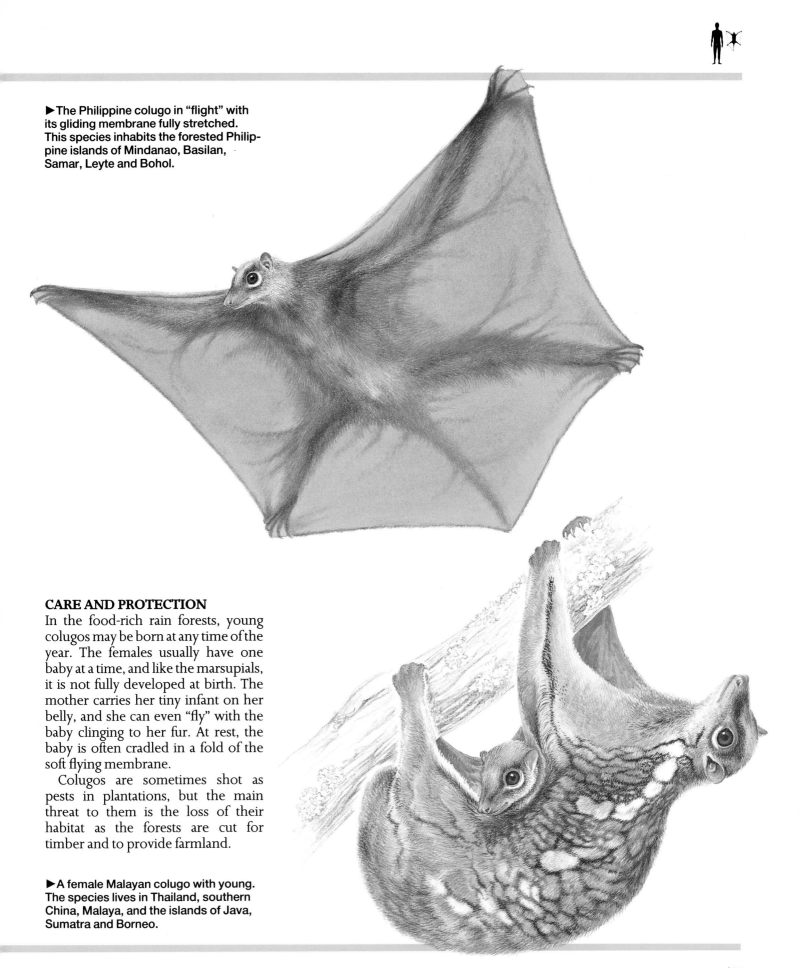

▶The Philippine colugo in "flight" with its gliding membrane fully stretched. This species inhabits the forested Philippine islands of Mindanao, Basilan, Samar, Leyte and Bohol.

CARE AND PROTECTION

In the food-rich rain forests, young colugos may be born at any time of the year. The females usually have one baby at a time, and like the marsupials, it is not fully developed at birth. The mother carries her tiny infant on her belly, and she can even "fly" with the baby clinging to her fur. At rest, the baby is often cradled in a fold of the soft flying membrane.

Colugos are sometimes shot as pests in plantations, but the main threat to them is the loss of their habitat as the forests are cut for timber and to provide farmland.

▶A female Malayan colugo with young. The species lives in Thailand, southern China, Malaya, and the islands of Java, Sumatra and Borneo.

BATS

It is the darkest time of night. The herd of cattle have settled down to rest. Out of the darkness comes the faint flutter of tiny wings. A vampire bat is swooping in for its night-time feed. It settles lightly on the shoulders of a young calf. With a swift movement of its tiny head, it slits the animal's hide with razor-sharp teeth. The calf doesn't feel a thing. The vampire's tongue then sets to work, flicking in and out of the wound as the blood starts oozing out.

►The Mexican Long-nosed bat uses its enormous tongue to reach the nectar in desert flowering plants such as cactus.

BATS Megachiroptera and Microchiroptera (*up to 1,000 species*)

● ■ ☠

◣ Habitat: general.

◪ Diet: most bats: insects; vampire bats: blood; flying foxes: fruit; also eaten by different species: nectar, spiders, frogs, lizards, fish, rodents.

◉ Breeding: varies, mostly 1 offspring per year; 2-3 offspring in some species; pregnancy lasts from 40 days, sometimes delayed up to 10 months.

Size: smallest (Kitti's hog-nosed bat): head-body 2.9cm, weight 1.5g; largest (flying foxes): head-body 40cm, weight 1.5kg.

Colour: mainly brown, grey and black, tinged red, yellow, orange, silver.

Lifespan: up to 30 years, average about 5 years.

Species mentioned in text:
Common vampire (*Desmodus rotundus*)
False vampire (*Vampyrum spectrum*)
Greater false vampire bat (*Megaderma lyra*)
Greater spear-nosed bat (*Phyllostomus hastatus*)
Hammer-headed bat (*Hypsignathus monstrosus*)
Kitti's hog-nosed bat (*Craseonycteris thonglongyai*)
Large mouse-eared bat (*Myotis myotis*)
Lesser mouse-tailed bat (*Rhinopoma hardwickei*)
Little brown bat (*Myotis lucifugus*)
Mexican long-nosed bat (*Leptonycteris nivalis*)
Natterer's bat (*Myotis nattereri*)
Samoan flying fox (*Pteropus samoensis*)
Schreiber's bent-winged bat (*Miniopterus schreibersi*)

►A Greater false vampire bat swoops on a mouse. It may take its catch back to its roost to eat it there.

A bat looks rather like a flying mouse. It is the only flying mammal. (The so-called flying squirrel does not fly but just glides, using flaps of skin between its feet.) The bat truly flies, flapping its wings like a bird.

BAD REPUTATION

The Common vampire bat is one of 1,000 species of bat living all around the globe, except in the polar regions. Almost all of the others are harmless and even useful creatures. They help keep down insect pests and vermin and pollinate plants and fruit trees.

But bats in general have had a bad reputation. People have killed them in huge numbers in the past. Today the biggest danger to bat species is the destruction and disturbance of their habitats by human activities.

WINGS AND FINGERS

A bat's wing is a thin membrane or layer of skin, supported by four long

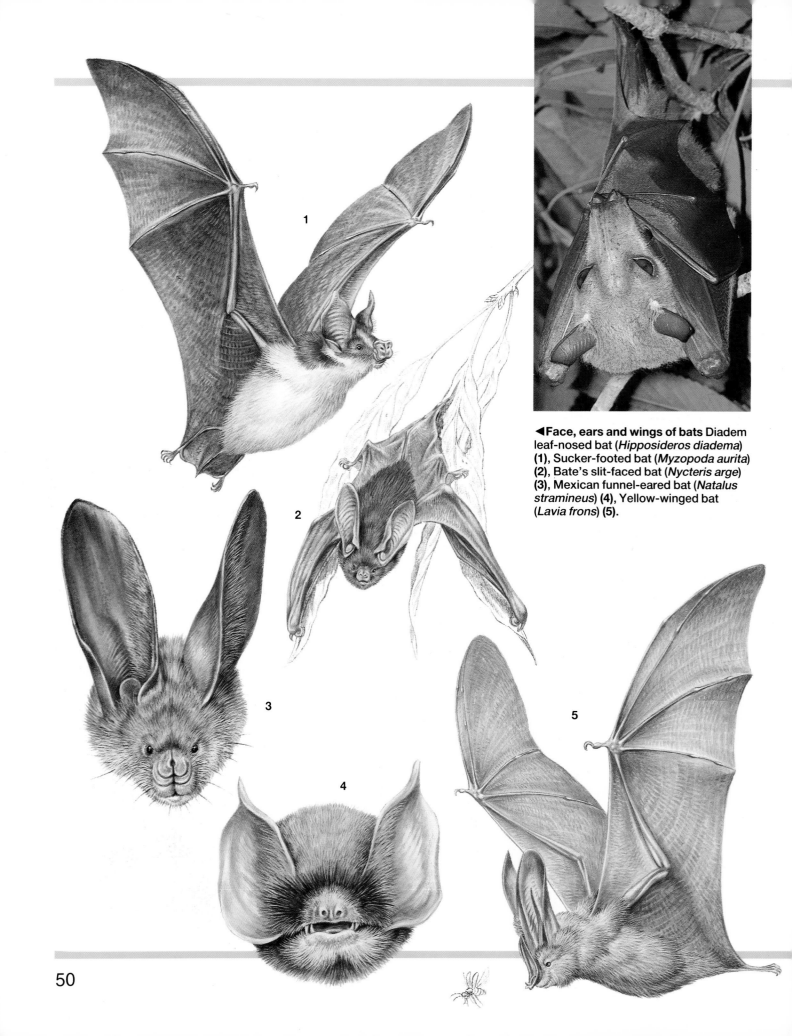

◄**Face, ears and wings of bats** Diadem leaf-nosed bat (*Hipposideros diadema*) **(1)**, Sucker-footed bat (*Myzopoda aurita*) **(2)**, Bate's slit-faced bat (*Nycteris arge*) **(3)**, Mexican funnel-eared bat (*Natalus stramineus*) **(4)**, Yellow-winged bat (*Lavia frons*) **(5)**.

bony fingers. A little clawed thumb protrudes at the front. The thumb is used mainly when the bat is moving around the roost. The wing membrane extends to the bat's legs and, in some species, between the legs to a tail. In other species, such as the Lesser mouse-tailed bat, the tail is free. Some flying foxes have no tail or tail membranes. The bat with the largest wingspan is believed to be the Samoan flying fox. Its wing tips can be as much as 1.5m apart.

In most species the legs are weak. The feet have five toes tipped with claws. Bats hang upside-down by their feet when roosting. The Common vampire bat has unusually strong legs. It can run and leap well.

SEEING BY SOUND
Bats sleep during the day in roosting places such as caves, old buildings and trees. They go foraging for food at dusk. Most bats eat insects, which they take on the wing. They have tiny eyes and rather poor eyesight (hence the expression "blind as a bat"). To "see" in the dark, bats rely mainly on sound. They find their way and detect their prey by echo-location or sonar.

When a bat goes in search of insects, it sends out pulses of ultrasound, sound waves too high-pitched for human ears to hear. Sending out about five pulses a second, the bat listens for any echoes. If it receives an echo reflected back from an insect, it increases the pulse rate up to about 200 pulses a second.

►The wing membranes of Davy's naked-backed bat (*Pteronotus davyi*) (1) reach over the back to meet in the middle. The Honduran disk-winged bat (*Thyroptera discifera*) (2). Both species are insect-eaters of the Americas.

From the echoes it receives back, the bat can pin-point exactly where the insect is and snatch it from the air. Usually this is done with the mouth, but the Natterer's bat and some other species first catch insects in their tail membrane.

Bats make these sounds through the open mouth or through the nostrils. The species that use their nostrils have complicated, often grotesque-looking noses. They include the leaf-nosed, hog-nosed, spear-nosed and horse-shoe bats. The "leaves" or flaps of skin on the nose help change and focus the sounds coming out.

The ears of bats that use sonar are also unusual. They are large, ridged and folded, which makes them receive the echoes clearly.

FRUIT-EATING BATS
Not all bats navigate and find their food by sonar. Most species of flying foxes use their eyes. These are large bats that feed mainly on fruit; they are often called fruit bats. They eat not only fruit, but also flowers and nectar.

This is how they provide a valuable service in pollinating the plants they visit and spreading the seeds.

Flying foxes look different from the small, odd-faced insect-eaters. They have a long face, large eyes and simple ears, spaced well apart. Their head does look rather like that of a fox. Their eyesight is very good, like that of birds, and they have a strong sense of smell.

Flying foxes are widespread in tropical and subtropical regions of Africa, India, South-east Asia and Australia. Only in the Americas are they absent. There, species of spear-nosed bats are the fruit-eaters.

CARNIVORES AND VAMPIRES
Other species of the spear-nosed bat family are carnivores, eating frogs, rodents and other small animals. Among them is the False vampire, the largest American bat, with a wingspan of up to 1m.

The Americas are also the home of the Common vampire. This bat's range extends from Mexico southwards to Argentina. The Common vampire feeds mostly on the blood of domesticated livestock, especially large herds of cattle. Attacks on humans are very rare. It takes only a little of an animal's blood and so does not harm it in that way. But the Common vampire can infect animals with diseases, including the deadly rabies.

BAT COLONIES

Bats feed mostly by night and roost by day. Flying foxes roost in the open, hanging from the branches of trees. Some bats nest in holes in trees, others in buildings, canal tunnels and other human constructions. The largest numbers of all roost in caves. Some colonies of cave-dwelling bats contain a million individuals or more.

Caves are ideal roosting places. They are safe and dark and have a steady temperature. With their skill at echo-location, bats have no problem finding their way around inside.

Among most species males and females roost together for much of the year. But some species roost in single-sex groups. There is not much pattern in the way bats mate, although there are a few exceptions. The Greater spear-nosed bat forms harems of females, with just one male mating with them.

Mating takes place at roost. Sometimes pregnancy is delayed until the climate is more suitable, maybe as long as 7 months after mating. Few other mammals do this. The young are sometimes born with their mother hanging upside-down. Otherwise the mother turns her head upwards and then catches the young in her tail membrane. The young begin suckling their mother almost immediately. In most bat colonies all the mothers and young roost together in a kind of nursery.

BEATING THE CLIMATE

In parts of the world where the climate is always warm, bats usually

stay active all the year. In the tropics bats may sleep through the hottest parts of the year. This period of sleep is called aestivation.

In cooler climates, bats have two main problems in winter. Their supply of food (notably insects) decreases; and the temperature falls. To cope with this, some bats migrate, making their way to warmer climates.

▲ Looking like a whirlwind, a huge colony of bats leave a cave in Java to feed at dusk.

▶ Red and naked, hundreds of newly born Schreiber's bent-winged bats on the roof of a nursery cave in Australia. They will remain in the cave for about 3 months.

◄A colony of fruit bats roosting during the daytime, their wings wrapped around them. In hot weather, they open out and flap their wings to keep cool.

▼Flying fox mother with newly born young. Three months may pass before it is ready to fly.

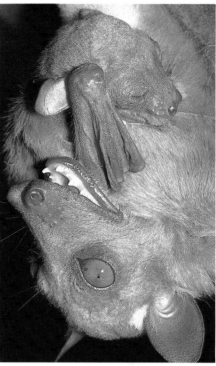

Others hibernate, sleeping through the winter cold.

Before they hibernate, these bats feed well to build up their body weight, including a thick layer of fat under the skin. Bats usually cluster together when they hibernate, which helps keep them warm. This can result in huge clusters of bats packed tightly together, with as many as 3,000 in a square metre. The Little brown bat of North America and the Large mouse-eared bat of Europe may hibernate together like this.

Hibernating bats do not spend the whole winter asleep. Every 10 days or so they wake up and sometimes fly a short distance to another site. This probably helps rid their bodies of wastes which build up and could otherwise poison them.

LEMURS

It's a stand-off. Two Ring-tailed lemurs face each other across a clearing on the forest floor. Angrily they wave their black-and-white-banded tails, heavily smeared in scent, high above their heads. This is a "stink fight". Scattered behind each of them is a family group, watching tensely. The two groups inhabit the same territory and often come up against each other. But suddenly, as if by a secret signal, the rival groups begin to drift apart.

Travelling through the forests of Madagascar, one will often see ghostly faces peering out through the branches. They are the faces of lemurs, a local word meaning "ghosts". They are not ghosts, of course, but furry, bushy-tailed animals.

Altogether there are over 20 species of lemurs. They all live on the island of Madagascar or on the nearby Comoro Islands.

Lemurs can be seen in almost all of the forests on Madagascar, but different species are found in different regions. The Ring-tailed lemur can be found throughout the island in the deciduous forests. Here most of the trees shed their leaves each year. The Western gentle lemur, on the other hand, is found only in bamboo forests along the western coast. The Brown lesser mouse lemur and the indri live only in the east, the one in forest fringes, the other in the rain forests.

The various species of lemur differ in size, colour and way of life. The Ring-tailed lemur is grey, while the Western gentle lemur is brown. Both are about the size of a grey squirrel. By contrast, the Brown lesser mouse lemur is mouse-size, while the indri, which has white fur, is nearly as big as a chimpanzee. Lemurs are primates, like monkeys and apes, but are not so highly developed or intelligent.

LEMURS Lemuridae, Cheirogaleidae, Indriidae, Daubentoniidae (*23 species*)

● ◨ 🦴

◿ **Habitat:** deciduous, rain or bamboo forest.

◨ **Diet:** mainly vegetarian – leaves, flowers, fruits; some insects.

◎ **Breeding:** mostly 1 offspring after pregnancy of 4-4½ months.

Size: smallest (mouse lemur): head-tail 26cm, weight 50g; largest (indri): head-tail 75cm, weight 10kg.

Colour: brown, white, black and white.

Lifespan: up to 18 years in captivity.

Species mentioned in text:
Aye-aye (*Daubentonia madagascariensis*)
Black lemur (*Lemur macaco*)
Brown lemur (*L. fulvus*)
Brown lesser mouse lemur (*Microcebus rufus*)
Fat-tailed dwarf lemur (*Cheirogaleus medius*)
Indri (*Indri indri*)
Mongoose lemur (*Lemur mongoz*)
Red-fronted lemur (*L. fulvus rufus*)
Ring-tailed lemur (*L. catta*)
Sifakas (*Propithecus verreauxi* and *P. diadema*)
Sportive lemur (*Lepilemur mustelinus*)
Western gentle lemur (*Hapalemur griseus occidentalis*)
Woolly lemur (*Avahi laniger*)

◀An indri in mid-leap showing its unique feature among the lemurs, a stumpy tail.

TYPICAL LEMURS

The Ring-tailed lemur is one of seven species of the so-called typical lemurs. These species are active during the day and feed on leaves, fruit and flowers. This group also includes the Brown, the Red-fronted and the Black lemur. They usually live together in small groups, but occasionally as many as 30 animals may be seen feeding together.

Most typical lemurs remain in the trees nearly all the time. They come down to the ground only where the forest thins out and they cannot leap across the gaps between trees. But the Ring-tailed lemur prefers to travel on all fours down on the ground.

The sense of smell is very important for lemurs. They often stop to smear branches with scent from glands in their body. These scent markings help "signpost" their territory and warn off other lemur groups. Lemurs also smear scent on their tail from glands on their wrists. Waving their scented tail plays an important part in their contests with their rivals.

BAMBOO EATERS

The Sportive lemur and the gentle lemurs behave differently from the typical lemurs. The Sportive lemur becomes active by night and sleeps

▲ **Some members of the lemur family**
All lemurs have long bushy tails. The muzzle is black and pointed and has sensitive whiskers. The Grey gentle lemur (*Hapalemur griseus griseus*) **(1)** marks a branch with scent glands on its wrists. The Brown lemur **(2)** marks its tail with scent. Also seen are the White-fronted lemur (*Lemur fulvus albifrons*) **(3)**, the Ruffed lemur (*Varecia variegata*) **(4)**, and the Sportive lemur **(5)**.

during the day. It also spends much of the time alone.

Sometimes a pair of Sportive lemurs share the same region of forest and come together several times a night to feed and occasionally groom each

other. They feed mainly on leaves. The gentle lemurs, though, have a limited diet, feeding only on bamboo shoots and reeds. Sometimes seen in small groups, they are most active in the morning and early afternoon. They use their hands a lot when they eat, to get at the tender inner parts of bamboo shoots and push them into the mouth.

THE SMALLEST PRIMATES

Dwarf and mouse lemurs are the smallest lemurs, and indeed are the smallest of all primates. The smallest mouse lemur weighs less than 50g even when fully grown. Both the dwarf and mouse lemurs are nocturnal. They have a much more varied diet than the other lemurs, eating beetles and other insects, as well as fruit, leaves and gum that comes out of the bark of trees.

Dwarf and mouse lemurs live alone for most of the time, except in the mating season. Unlike most other lemurs, they usually give birth to two or three offspring.

When food is plentiful, in the wet season, mouse lemurs build up fat in their rump and tail. This store helps them survive in the drier months when food becomes scarce. Dwarf lemurs store fat in the same way. But

▲▼Among the lemurs, the Ring-tailed lemur is easiest to recognize. No other lemur has a tail quite like it. In a "stink fight" the lemur rubs scent on its tail, then shakes it back and forth to waft the smell towards its rival.

they become dormant, or sleep, through the dry months.

LEAPS, HOOTS AND RATTLES

Most lemurs move through the leafy branches of the forest by leaping. But the name "leaping lemurs" is usually given to the large lemurs of the indri family. They include the indri itself, the Woolly lemur and the sifakas.

These animals are truly master-leapers. They launch themselves through the air in an upright position, with arms outstretched, from tree trunk to tree trunk. The indri has been seen to make leaps of up to 10m. It also has an odd way of walking on the few occasions it descends to the ground. It hops on its hind legs, holding its arms in the air.

The leaping lemurs live together in small groups. They mark their territory with their scent and give out frequent loud howls. They use different calls to warn of danger. The indri hoots and roars; sifakas make a noise like a football rattle.

LEMURS AT RISK

All the lemurs live and feed in the forests, and they are affected when the trees are cut down for timber or to increase farmland. Some species are already scarce and are found only in small areas of Madagascar. Most at risk at present is the aye-aye, which lives in the rain forests of the eastern coast.

The gentle lemurs are also becoming scarce. This is mainly because their diet of bamboo shoots and reeds is found in only a few places. The other lemurs stand a better chance of surviving because they eat a variety of food. Sifakas suffer more directly from human contact. Local people trap and shoot them for food.

1

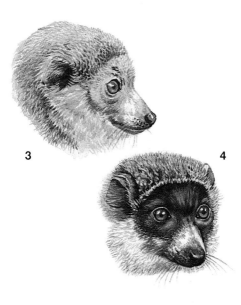

2

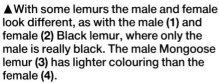

3

4

▲With some lemurs the male and female look different, as with the male (1) and female (2) Black lemur, where only the male is really black. The male Mongoose lemur (3) has lighter colouring than the female (4).

◀The Fat-tailed dwarf lemur, so called because it stores fat in its tail, is a slow-moving animal.

BUSH BABIES AND LORISES

In a dense forest in Gabon, late in the evening, an urgent call suddenly pierces the darkness: "Ngok! Nogkoué!" It is the alarm call of a bush baby high in the tree canopy. Some large animal is passing near by, and the bush baby senses danger.

BUSH BABIES AND LORISES
Lorisidae (*10 species*)

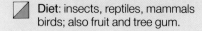

△ Habitat: tropical rain forest, dry forest, savannah with trees.

◩ Diet: insects, reptiles, mammals birds; also fruit and tree gum.

◯ Breeding: usually 1 offspring after pregnancy of 4-6 months.

Size: smallest (Dwarf bush baby): head-tail 29cm, weight 60g; largest (Thick-tailed bush baby): head-tail 76cm, weight 1.2kg.

Colour: grey to reddish-brown.

Lifespan: up to 15 years in captivity.

Species mentioned in text:
Allen's bush baby (*Galago alleni*)
Dwarf bush baby (*G. demidovii*)
Golden potto, or angwantibo
   (*Arctocebus calabarensis*)
Lesser bush baby (*Galago senegalensis*)
Needle-clawed bush baby
   (*G. elegantulus* W. Africa and
   G. inustus C. Africa)
Potto (*Perodicticus potto*)
Slender loris (*Loris tardigradus*)
Slow loris (*Nycticebus coucang*)

Bush babies live only in Africa, but are found widely there. Allen's bush baby lives in the tropical rain forests of West Africa. So do the Needle-clawed bush baby and the Dwarf bush baby. The latter can also be found much farther afield, on the coast of Kenya in the east. The most widespread species of all, however, is the Lesser bush baby. This can be found in wet and dry forests and open woodland from Senegal to Angola in the west and from Ethiopia to Mozambique in the north and east.

Pottos are also found widely in the West African rain forests. Lorises, however, live in Asia. The Slender loris is found in India and Sri Lanka, the Slow loris over a vast area from Bangladesh in the north to Indonesia in the south.

FAST MOVERS
Bush babies are well named. They look appealing and have sad cries. They are also sometimes called galagos after their scientific genus name. Like the lorises and pottos, they are primates and are related to the lemurs of Madagascar.

Bush babies, like all creatures of the night, have large eyes. They also have large ears with which they can detect the slightest sounds. They use their sensitive ears when hunting for insects such as moths, which make up much of their diet. When a moth flies by, they clamp their feet around a branch. Stretching out their body, they snatch the moth out of the air with one or both hands.

The arms of bush babies are quite short, while the hind legs are long and muscular. This tells us that they should be good at leaping, and so they are. They can move rapidly through the leafy canopy of the forest and are usually able to escape from animals that hunt them. Their long bushy tail helps steady them as they jump.

In Gabon, Allen's bush baby is known as Ngok or Nogkoué, after its

alarm call when a dangerous animal such as a leopard passes near by. Bush babies are in general very vocal during the night as they spread out to feed. They call to keep in contact with other members of their group. In the early morning a rallying call brings them together so that they can sleep as a group.

SLOW CLIMBERS
Pottos and lorises are close relatives of bush babies. But instead of being swift jumpers they are slow climbers. They move as though in slow motion through the thick forests they live in. This makes them very difficult to see. When they are scared by a sudden sound, they freeze. They can remain in a fixed position for hours if need be until danger has passed.

Pottos and lorises have large eyes because they are nocturnal, like bush babies. But, unlike bush babies, all four of their limbs are about the same length, and they have only a stumpy tail. They feed on slow-moving creatures, such as caterpillars and beetles. They hunt out their prey with their nose, for they have a well-developed sense of smell.

Being slow movers, pottos and lorises could become easy prey themselves for hunters like the civet. But they can defend themselves quite well. The potto uses a hump of thick skin on its shoulder as a shield to defend itself. The Golden potto rolls itself up into a ball. Both pottos can bite fiercely when attacked.

NOT ENDANGERED
Because of their small size and nocturnal habits, bush babies, lorises and pottos are not hunted as much as other primates in the countries where they live. In fact, few people have seen these animals in the wild and, except in those areas where their forest homes are being destroyed, there is little that threatens their survival.

1

2

3

4

5

►**Moving about in the trees.** Like the other bush babies, the Thick-tailed bush baby (*Galago crassicaudatus*) **(1)** travels rapidly by leaping. Its relatives, the lorises and pottos, are climbers, moving slowly along the branches. They include the Slow loris **(2)**, the Slender loris **(3)**, the potto **(4)** and the Golden potto **(5)**. Their hands and feet have a strong pincer-like grip.

MARMOSETS AND TAMARINS

It is just after dawn in a coastal forest of Brazil. Resting in a cosy hole in one of the tall trees is a family of Golden lion tamarins. All at once, the peace is shattered by the roar of a chain saw. Startled, the mother and father, each carrying one of their twin babies, scamper around in panic, then head into the forest, away from the noise. But worse is to come. In their headlong flight from the din, they don't hear the poachers. Two shots ring out, and the parents are dead. The poachers snatch the babies, still clinging in terror to their parents' bodies. The babies will fetch a good price at market.

Poaching and the destruction of forests have made the Golden lion tamarin almost extinct in the wild. Fewer than 100 may remain. The same is true for a close relative, the Golden-rumped lion tamarin. Other tamarins and some species of marmosets are also becoming rare because of human interference.

Marmosets and tamarins are the smallest of the monkeys that live in the Americas. They mostly inhabit the thick forests of the River Amazon basin in Brazil. Some live in more open savannah-type country in Paraguay and Bolivia. Others are found as far north as Costa Rica in Central America.

Because of their attractive appearance, marmosets and tamarins have long been in demand as pets and for zoos. They have a fine, silky, often colourful coat. Some have a mane, some a crest and others the most splendid drooping moustaches.

The rare Golden lion tamarin's bright gold mane, like a male lion's, makes it one of the most striking creatures on Earth. The Cotton-top tamarin of Columbia has a pure white crest that cascades to its shoulders. Among the moustached tamarins, the Emperor tamarin has an impressive white beard.

A STICKY DIET

Both marmosets and tamarins have a varied diet, feeding on plants, insects and other animals. They also feed on the gum oozing from trees. This often occurs when the trees are bored into by insects. Marmosets, however, don't need to rely on insects to hole the trees. They can gouge out holes themselves. When they want to make a hole, they sink their long upper incisor teeth into the bark and then gouge upwards with their lower ones, which act like a chisel.

The Pygmy marmoset feeds on gum more than the other marmosets. Like them, it has claws on all its fingers and toes, except for the big toes. This helps it cling to the tree trunk while feeding.

FAMILY GROUPS

Marmosets and tamarins go around in small family groups of mother, father and their offspring. Only one female in the group breeds, even though there may be several others present. She gives birth usually twice a year and frequently to twins.

When it comes to looking after the baby, every member of the group helps out, including the father. All the group also help to feed the mother, as well as the infants and other group members that are carrying them.

▶Marmosets and tamarins Goeldi's monkey (*Callimico goeldii*) (1) and the Black-tailed marmoset (*Callithrix argentata melanura*) (2) are shown in offensive pose. Geoffroy's tamarin (*Saguinus geoffroyi*) (3), the Red-chested moustached tamarin (*Saguinus labiatus*) (4) and the Saddle-back tamarin (*Saguinus fuscicollis*) (5) are seen scent-marking. The Golden-rumped lion tamarin (6) has a long flowing mane, while the Tassel-ear marmoset (*Callithrix humeralifer intermedius*) (7) has a red muzzle. The smallest marmoset, the Pygmy (8), gouges a tree for gum.

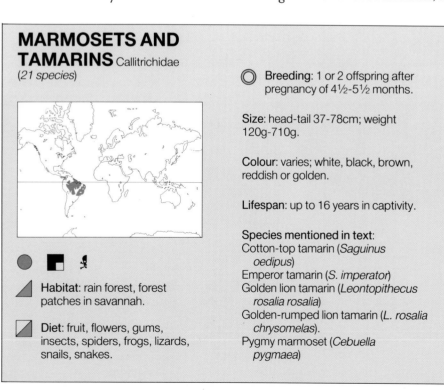

MARMOSETS AND TAMARINS Callitrichidae
(*21 species*)

◯ Breeding: 1 or 2 offspring after pregnancy of 4½-5½ months.

Size: head-tail 37-78cm; weight 120g-710g.

Colour: varies; white, black, brown, reddish or golden.

Lifespan: up to 16 years in captivity.

Species mentioned in text:
Cotton-top tamarin (*Saguinus oedipus*)
Emperor tamarin (*S. imperator*)
Golden lion tamarin (*Leontopithecus rosalia rosalia*)
Golden-rumped lion tamarin (*L. rosalia chrysomelas*).
Pygmy marmoset (*Cebuella pygmaea*)

▲ Habitat: rain forest, forest patches in savannah.

▱ Diet: fruit, flowers, gums, insects, spiders, frogs, lizards, snails, snakes.

CAPUCHIN MONKEYS

The Sun sets over the vast Amazon jungle. For 50 species of monkey it is time to sleep. But in thick tangled vines and holes in trees another monkey species is stirring. As darkness falls, Night monkeys spread out, foraging almost silently for food. Then the sky begins to lighten, as a brilliant full Moon rises. The hooting starts – it is a group of male Night monkeys. They are declaring their territory and warning off other males.

The tropical forests of the Amazon basin are the home of the Night monkey and of many other species of the capuchin family. These include not only the capuchin monkeys themselves, but also Squirrel monkeys, titis, sakis, uakaris and spider monkeys. The capuchin family are often called cebids, after the Latin family name.

The Night monkey and Squirrel monkey are found throughout tropical South America and in Central America. Other monkeys of the capuchin family have a considerably narrower range. The Yellow-tailed woolly monkey, for example, is found only in one mountainous region in Peru.

Capuchin monkeys are named after Capuchin monks. This is because they have a cap of hair on the crown of the head which looks like a monk's cowl or hood. The monkeys are among the most intelligent of all the primates and are easily trained as pets and to perform tricks.

COMPETITION FOR FOOD
Several different species of monkeys often live in the same region of forest, sharing the food the forest provides.

▶Like its parents, this baby Smoky woolly monkey is covered from head to toe in long thick fur. When older, its coat may turn grey or brown, but its head will remain dark.

CAPUCHIN MONKEYS
Cebidae (*30 species*)

⬤ ◼ ⚔

◢ **Habitat:** tropical and subtropical evergreen forest.

◪ **Diet:** fruit, roots, leaves, insects, small mammals, snails, spiders.

◎ **Breeding:** 1 offspring after pregnancy of 4-7½ months.

Size: smallest (Squirrel monkey): head-tail 62cm, weight 600g; largest (Woolly spider monkey): head-tail 137cm, weight 12kg.

Colour: varies; white, yellow, red-brown, black, often with patterning around head.

Lifespan: up to 25 years.

Species mentioned in text:
Brown capuchin (*Cebus apella*)
Mexican black howler (*Alouatta villosa*)
Night monkey (*Aotus trivirgatus*)
Smoky, or Humboldt's woolly monkey (*Lagothrix lagotricha*)
Squirrel monkey (*Saimiri sciureus*)
White-faced saki (*Pithecia pithecia*)
Woolly spider monkey or muriqui (*Brachyteles arachnoides*)
Yellow-tailed woolly monkey (*Lagothrix flavicauda*)

▲Capuchin monkeys moving through the trees The bushy-tailed White-faced saki (1) and stumpy-tailed Red uakari (*Cacajao rubicundus*) (2) climb through the branches on all fours. The Dusky titi (*Callicebus moloch*) (3) and Squirrel monkey (4) travel mainly by leaping. The Black howler monkey (*Alouatta caraya*) (5), Black-handed spider monkey (*Ateles geoffroyi*) (6) and Smoky woolly monkey (7) use their tails as well as their hands. The animals shown are all females. The males are slightly bigger.

▶The Woolly spider monkey is the largest and most ape-like of the New World monkeys. It swings by its tail and arms.

This can sometimes lead to as many as five different species feeding on the same tree. As is to be expected, there is usually a fight to see which one will have the best of the food.

The big monkeys usually win, but not always. The Squirrel monkey relies on safety in numbers, going about in large groups of 30 to 40. Such numbers are usually more than a

match for the small groups of large monkeys that might threaten them. The Night monkey has overcome the competition by adapting to a nocturnal life. It feeds while its rivals sleep.

Other small monkeys have taken to a more specialized diet. The titis are able to eat fruit while it is still green, which the big monkeys will not touch. The bearded sakis can open the seeds of fruits and eat what is inside.

LEAPERS AND SWINGERS
Cebids spend almost all their time in the trees. Only occasionally do they drop to the ground to play, search for

food or travel between stands of trees. Up in the trees they move about by leaping, climbing and swinging on their arms. The leapers, such as the Squirrel monkey, have long powerful hind legs for launching themselves into the air.

The "swingers", such as the spider monkeys, have long arms and move hand over hand below the branches. They have specially developed shoulder-joints that help them swivel easily. Their most interesting feature is the tail, which is long and flexible. Known as a prehensile tail, the monkeys use it as a fifth limb to grip branches and to steady themselves. They may even hang from it, leaving their hands free to reach food.

BREEDING PAIRS
Most of the smaller cebids, such as the Night monkey, the titis and the sakis, live in small family groups, based on a male and female pair. The pair stay together, raising one infant each year. The young stays with the parents until after the next offspring arrives.

The small Squirrel monkey, living in much larger groups, is an exception. Each group contains several breeding males and females. Vicious fights break out in the breeding season between the males. In some of the larger species, the males keep a harem of several females.

SAFETY IN NUMBERS
Spider monkeys and capuchin monkeys also often live together in groups of up to 20. Monkeys belonging to a large group are less likely to suffer from attacks by predators. These include a variety of hawks and eagles. When a group is large, there are more eyes and ears to watch and listen and to raise the alarm when danger threatens.

A large group size also helps in the constant search for food. Individual monkeys in the group may know of different food trees and when they are

▲Young Squirrel monkeys spend much of their time playing. They wrestle (1) and spar (2) with one another, explore holes in trees (3), stalk birds (4) and try to catch insects (5). All these activities help prepare them for adult life.

in fruit. A large group can also send out more "scouts" to look for new fruit trees. When a member of a Brown capuchin group finds a new tree, it lets out a loud whistle to call the others.

Another advantage is that a large group can usually chase monkeys of smaller groups away from the best food trees. It can also defend the trees better.

Sometimes different groups live peacefully together. Groups of Squirrel monkeys do not usually fight even when they feed on the same trees. They may also join up with groups of Brown capuchins to feed, again without any fighting.

PECKING ORDER

Life in most groups is well organized. Most activities centre around looking for food and raising young. There is nearly always a "pecking order" among the members of the group. The leader is usually a dominant male. The social position of other group members depends on how well they get along with him.

The pecking order is often important at feeding time. In a Brown capuchin group, the "boss" and his favourites usually feed first. He positions himself inside a ring of other monkeys so as to be safer from predators. The monkeys not in his favour may have to wait until he and his select group have finished eating and moved on.

REARING INFANTS

Most members of a group share in raising the young. A new mother is helped by females that do not have offspring of their own. These monkeys help carry the young and also "baby-sit" while the mother goes off to feed.

In some species, including the Squirrel monkey, the males play little part in family life. But in species which live in small family groups the males

▲ The Squirrel monkey sometimes eats flowers as well as its usual diet of fruit and insects.

▼ A family group of titi monkeys. When resting, titis huddle together and entwine their tails (1). The father often grooms the young (2).

A pair of White-faced sakis. Only the male (left) has a white face. They will probably spend most of their life together in a small family group.

help out. In the small family groups of the titi monkeys, the young often spend more time with their father than with their mother. The father carries the youngest most of the time and spends hours grooming it.

THE SUCCESSFUL HOWLERS

Most monkey groups take part in the dawn chorus of the jungle. They call at other times during the day to announce where they are and to warn off other groups near by. The loudest monkeys by far are the six species of howler monkey.

By passing air through an enlarged bone in their throat, they can let out the most penetrating howl. It can carry for over a kilometre, even through thick forest. The loudness of their howl helps individuals and groups keep in touch with each other and has helped make them successful as a species. Howlers have the widest range of all the primates in the New World. The Mexican black howler is found as far north as Yucatan in Mexico, the Black howler as far south as Argentina.

Another reason for the howlers'

success is that when fruit and flowers are not available they can eat leaves. They can live on leaves for weeks, something most other species of monkey would find difficult.

Howlers are able to survive on leaves because of their modified gut, in which the leaves are digested. They help themselves by choosing tender young leaves which break down more quickly. However, leaves are not very nutritious and do not provide much energy. As a result, howlers are quite slow moving animals and spend half the day resting or sleeping.

LONG-TERM PROSPECTS

More than 10 species of Capuchin monkeys are endangered. In the Amazon basin, spider monkeys and woolly monkeys have been shot for food over much of their range. One species is now confined to just seven small areas of forest and its numbers have fallen to less than 250. However, species such as the Night monkey and Squirrel monkey can adapt quite easily to a loss and change of habitat. If more of their forest homes are protected, their survival can be assured.

▲Looking almost like a parrot here, this male Night monkey is looking for a mate. He may travel more than 5km on his nightly travels.

MACAQUES

One of Gibraltar's two troops of Barbary apes are resting quietly on a rocky hillside. They are huddled together in small groups of males, females and babies. Trouble seems to be brewing in one group as one male threatens another. But the threatened male doesn't fight. Instead he picks up one of the babies by the leg and offers it upside-down to the other male. This gesture quickly restores peace and both males start lip-smacking and teeth-chattering over the baby.

MACAQUES
Cercopithecidae (*15 species*)

● ■ ☠

◣ **Habitat:** lowland and highland forest, scrubland, cliffs, swamps.

◺ **Diet:** fruit, leaves, crops, insects.

◯ **Breeding:** 1 offspring after pregnancy of about 5 months.

Size: varies; head-body 50-70cm; weight 5.1kg female, 7.9kg male (Stump-tailed macaque).

Colour: mostly light or dark brown or grey; sometimes with a coloured rump.

Lifespan: up to 30 years.

Species mentioned in text:
Barbary ape or macaque (*Macaca sylvanus*)
Crab-eating macaque (*M. fascicularis*)
Japanese macaque (*M. fuscata*)
Père David's macaque (*M. thibetana*)
Rhesus monkey or macaque (*M. mulatta*)

The so-called Barbary apes are not in fact apes, but macaques. In North Africa they inhabit the high forests, scrubland and cliffs of the Atlas mountains. They were brought to Gibraltar by British soldiers in 1740.

Barbary apes are hardy creatures. Their thick fur helps them survive in the cold winters of the mountains. Lip-smacking and teeth-chattering are normal behaviour among males, who play an important part in looking after babies and infants within or outside their own group. They protect them when danger threatens and carry and groom them.

MACAQUES OF ASIA
Other macaques are hardy mountain dwellers too, living in Asia. They include the Japanese macaque, Père David's macaque of Tibet and China and the Rhesus monkey, which ranges all through the foothills of the Himalayas, from Afghanistan to China.

1

More species of macaques live in the rain forests of the tropics, in Borneo, the Philippines and Indonesia. Among these tropical species is the Crab-eating macaque, which makes its home in swamps and coastal forests and does indeed sometimes eat crabs.

USED FOR SCIENCE

The Rhesus monkey is one of the most wide-ranging and most plentiful of the macaques. It is also the one most widely studied. For many years it has been the monkey most used in laboratory experiments for medical research.

Research scientists use the Rhesus monkey to test the effectiveness of drugs against diseases. (Like its close relatives, the mangabeys, guenons and baboons, the Rhesus monkey can catch many human diseases, including tuberculosis and yellow fever.) This helps scientists discover how the drugs will affect human beings.

Once it was thought that trapping of

Rhesus monkeys for export for medical research might one day wipe out the species. But this now seems unlikely, because many laboratory animals are bred in captivity, and research using animals has declined.

UNDER THREAT

One major threat these days comes from farmers. In some regions Rhesus monkeys and other macaques live on the forest edges and often go into the cultivated fields to feed on the crops. When a troop of up to 70 animals gets to work, the crops are devastated. So the farmers go hunting to reduce the monkey population.

5

2

4

3

▲▶**Facial expressions** A male Barbary ape **(1)** "lip-smacks" as it holds an infant, perhaps its own or another male's offspring. A Moor macaque (*Macaca maura*) **(2)** and a Stump-tailed macaque (*Macaca arctoides*) **(3)** open their mouths threateningly. A Pig-tailed macaque (*Macaca nemestrina*) **(4)** makes a pout-face, often seen before two macaques mate or groom each other. A Rhesus monkey **(5)** stares aggressively.

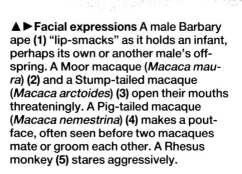

◀The Japanese macaque is a hardy species. Its thick shaggy coat keeps it warm in the cold snowy winters of northern Japan.

BABOONS

A group of about 30 Hamadryas baboons are picking their way through the stony desert landscape. A male near the front of the ragged line looks round to see if the rest of the group is keeping up. He sees one of the females lagging behind and dashes down the line towards her. Seeing him coming, she hurries to catch up. But it is too late. He sinks his teeth into the back of her neck and shakes her angrily. Squealing, she follows him closely back into line.

The Hamadryas baboon lives in very large troops, sometimes of more than 200 animals. A small group of 30 may form a clan of perhaps three families. A number of clans group into a band of 80 or 90 animals, and several bands join together to form the troop.

The smallest group, the family unit, is a harem, led by a male. The leader is followed by his female mate, their daughters and a few male "hangers on". Some of these quietly join the clan to court the young females and in time attract them away to start a

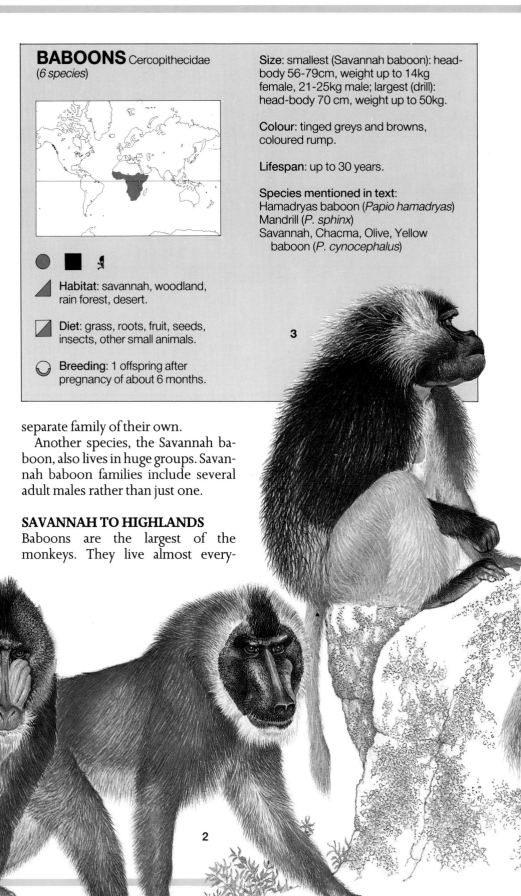

BABOONS Cercopithecidae
(*6 species*)

Size: smallest (Savannah baboon): head-body 56-79cm, weight up to 14kg female, 21-25kg male; largest (drill): head-body 70 cm, weight up to 50kg.

Colour: tinged greys and browns, coloured rump.

Lifespan: up to 30 years.

Species mentioned in text:
Hamadryas baboon (*Papio hamadryas*)
Mandrill (*P. sphinx*)
Savannah, Chacma, Olive, Yellow baboon (*P. cynocephalus*)

Habitat: savannah, woodland, rain forest, desert.

Diet: grass, roots, fruit, seeds, insects, other small animals.

Breeding: 1 offspring after pregnancy of about 6 months.

separate family of their own.

Another species, the Savannah baboon, also lives in huge groups. Savannah baboon families include several adult males rather than just one.

SAVANNAH TO HIGHLANDS

Baboons are the largest of the monkeys. They live almost everywhere in Africa where there is water to drink.

The Savannah or Common baboon is widespread in the grasslands and bush and along forest edges from Ethiopia to South Africa. There are three different forms of the Savannah baboon, each from a different region. They are recognizable by the colour of their coat. The Yellow baboon (its coat is yellowish-grey) lives in lowland East and Central Africa; the Olive baboon (olive green-grey) in the East African highlands, and the Chacma baboon (with a dark grey coat) in southern Africa.

The Hamadryas baboon lives in Ethiopia and neighbouring Somalia and, across the Red Sea, in Saudi Arabia and South Yemen. It is found in rocky desert areas of scattered grass and thorn bush.

COLOURFUL FEATURES

Baboons have a naked face and a muzzle rather like that of a dog. Males and females can often be recognized by their coat. The adult male Hamadryas baboon, for example, has long silvery-grey hair, forming a kind of cape over its shoulders. The female's coat is brown.

One can also identify the sexes by the colour of the face. Females have a black face, males a bright red one. The males also have a distinctive bright red rump.

The mandrill is the most colourful among baboon males. Its face is marked red and blue, and its bare rump is blue to purple. The female has similar but duller colouring and is only half the male's size.

When they are ready to mate, adult female baboons develop swellings on their rump and thighs. Each individual has a characteristic pattern of swellings.

◀**Drills and baboons** Red-and-blue-faced mandrill **(1)** Drill (*Papio leucophaeus*) **(2)** Gelada (*Theropithecus gelada*) **(3)** showing bare patches on its neck and chest. Hamadryas baboon **(4)**, with red naked skin on its face and rump. Guinea baboon (*Papio papio*) **(5)**. Olive baboon **(6)**, a form of the Savannah or Common baboon, of highland East Africa, shown with its dead prey, a hare. Chacma baboon **(7)** another form of the Savannah baboon, of southern Africa. Each example is of the adult male.

GIBBONS

It is two hours after sunrise in the dense forest on one of the Mentawai Islands of Indonesia. A family of Kloss gibbons are feeding in the tree-tops. The male raises his head to whistle and sing, warning other males off his territory. He has been doing this, on and off, since before dawn. Soon it is the female's turn. Her song is even more musical, made up of long falling and rising notes and tuneful trills. During her final trills, she starts swinging through the branches, tearing off leaves. The rest of the family join in noisily.

▼A White-handed gibbon in a typical gibbon position, hanging by its long arms. Both males and females look alike.

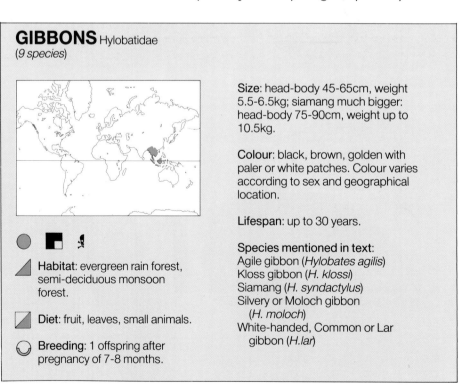

Gibbons are the only apes that live on the mainland of Asia. They are found from Bangladesh to Vietnam and along the Malay peninsula. They inhabit the islands of Sumatra and Borneo, along with the other Asian ape, the orang-utan.

Gibbons are much smaller and more lightly built than the orang-utan and the other great apes (chimpanzees and gorillas). They are often called the lesser apes. The two sexes are similar in size.

Like all the apes, they have no tail, and their arms are long. They often stand upright and can walk well on two legs, even along branches of trees. But their usual method of moving through the trees is by swinging, hand over hand, below the branches.

Most species of gibbons are about the same size. The exception is the siamang, which is nearly twice the size of the others. The siamang is completely black, as is the Kloss gibbon. More colourful is the Agile gibbon, which is light buff, with gold, reds and browns, and white cheeks and eye-

▲A siamang calls loudly from a bamboo thicket. The balloon-like sac on its throat makes the call resound and carry farther.

brows. There are some colour differences between males and females of the same species.

LIFE-LONG MATE
The everyday life of the gibbon is centred around the family. Adult gibbons choose a mate for life, and produce young every 2 to 3 years. The

GIBBONS Hylobatidae
(9 species)

Size: head-body 45-65cm, weight 5.5-6.5kg; siamang much bigger: head-body 75-90cm, weight up to 10.5kg.

Colour: black, brown, golden with paler or white patches. Colour varies according to sex and geographical location.

Lifespan: up to 30 years.

Species mentioned in text:
Agile gibbon (*Hylobates agilis*)
Kloss gibbon (*H. klossi*)
Siamang (*H. syndactylus*)
Silvery or Moloch gibbon (*H. moloch*)
White-handed, Common or Lar gibbon (*H.lar*)

Habitat: evergreen rain forest, semi-deciduous monsoon forest.

Diet: fruit, leaves, small animals.

Breeding: 1 offspring after pregnancy of 7-8 months.

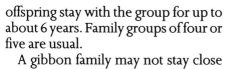

offspring stay with the group for up to about 6 years. Family groups of four or five are usual.

A gibbon family may not stay close together during the day. The animals go off on their own to feed. They come together from time to time to rest and groom, and many also sleep together.

FIERCE DEFENDERS

More than any other ape, gibbons are fierce defenders of their home territory. Both the male and female in a family group call loudly to warn others off. Their calls can be complicated and tuneful and are often described as songs. Each species of gibbon can be identified by the kind of song it sings. Male and female gibbons of most species perform a duet together, but the male and female Kloss gibbon sing solo.

◄A female Kloss gibbon launches herself into the air as she finishes her great call. Her baby, clinging to her belly, joins in.

▼The Silvery gibbon is named after its silvery-grey coat. Like several other gibbons, it is in danger of extinction because of logging operations.

CHIMPANZEES

Two groups of chimpanzees meet for the first time in days. They know one another, but there is tension in the air. A male from one group suddenly gets up and charges towards the other group. None of the opposing males wants to accept his challenge today.

▼The face and ears of the adult Common chimpanzee are brownish-black. When it was young, they would have been pink.

The two species of chimpanzee both live in tropical Africa. The Common chimpanzee is found in West and Central Africa, north of the River Zaire. It inhabits thick forest and also more open savannah country.

The Pygmy chimpanzee, or bonobo, is found only in the rain forests of Zaire. Although called "Pygmy" it is not noticeably smaller than the Common species, but it is of slighter build. One main difference between the two species is in face colour. The Common chimpanzee has a pink to brown face, the Pygmy chimpanzee an all-black one.

Both species spend much of the time on the ground. They sometimes walk upright on two feet, but they usually walk on all fours, using the knuckle not the palm of each hand.

STICKS AND STONES

Like the other apes, chimpanzees are mainly vegetarian, and they prefer to eat ripe fruit. But they also kill and eat animals such as monkeys, baboons, pigs and antelopes.

CHIMPANZEES
Pongidae (*2 species*)

● ■ ☠

Habitat: tropical rain forest, deciduous forest, mixed savannah.

Diet: fruit, leaves, flowers, seeds, some animals.

Breeding: 1 offspring after a pregnancy of 7½-8 months.

Size: head-body 70-85cm, weight 30kg female; head-body 70-90cm, weight 40kg male.

Colour: coat black, greying with age.

Lifespan: up to 45 years.

Species mentioned in text:
Common chimpanzee (*Pan troglodytes*)
Pygmy chimpanzee or bonobo (*P. paniscus*)

Chimpanzees eat insects as well, such as caterpillars and ants. To reach ants inside a nest, they bring their stick-tools into action. They put the sticks into the nest and wait for the ants to crawl up. Chimpanzees also use sticks and sometimes stones to crack open fruit shells that are too hard to bite.

Once it was thought that only human beings used tools. But this use of sticks and stones shows how intelligent chimpanzees are. In fact, with gorillas, they are the second most intelligent creatures on Earth, after humans. Chimpanzees in captivity have learned to use some of the hand signals of the sign language of hearing impaired people.

GANG WARFARE

Every chimpanzee belongs to a large loose group or community of perhaps as many as 120 animals. Some live alone for much of the time, but most travel in small groups. There are mixed-sex family groups and also all-male groups of up to 12 that are a threat to other groups because they challenge the breeding males.

Displays of charging and stick throwing take place regularly in chimpanzee groups. They are usually performed by the strongest or most aggressive male as a challenge to other males. If they still accept him as boss, they bob up and down, panting and grunting. But if a male takes up the challenge, a noisy fight breaks out until one or the other runs away.

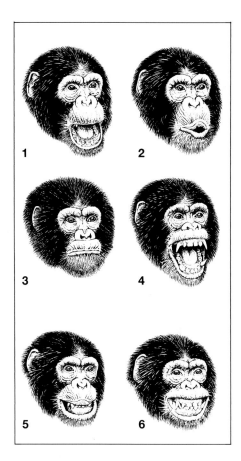

▶The chimpanzee has one of the most expressive faces of all primates. (1) The relaxed play face. (2) The pout, used when begging for food. (3) The display face, which shows aggression. (4) The full open grin, showing fear or excitement. (5) The horizontal pout, showing surrender after being attacked. (6) The fear grin, displayed when approaching an animal of higher rank.

▼Chimpanzees are threatened by destruction of their forest homes and by hunting for bushmeat.

ORANG-UTAN

A shaggy haired creature nearly as big as a man is swinging slowly through the branches of the tangled Borneo forest. It is the most colourful of the apes, the orang-utan. From time to time it stops to feed on insects or to raid a bird's nest. Then it continues on its way. After a few hours it arrives at its destination, a fig tree in full fruit. Drawing on its excellent memory and knowledge of the forest, the orang-utan knew exactly where to go. It also knew the exact time when the fruit would be ripe.

The orang-utan is a large, red, long-haired ape. It is found only on the islands of Sumatra and Borneo in South-east Asia. The name orang-utan means "man of the woods" in the Malay language. Those in Sumatra are thinner and have longer faces than the ones in Borneo. They also have a paler coat with longer hair.

The male adult orang-utan is very different in size and appearance from the female. He is almost twice as big and has large cheek flaps of fatty tissue. He also has a bag-like pouch hanging from the throat. When he makes his "long call", the air bag inflates and makes the call resound.

Adults' faces are bare and black, while the young have a pale muzzle and rings around the eyes.

▲A mother orang-utan and her infant. She will probably raise only three or four offspring during her 20 years of motherhood. At one time, mother orang-utans were shot to capture their young for use as pets.

▼A male orang-utan making his "long call". He breaks a branch off a tree and hurls it to the ground. Then he lets out a series of loud roars, bellows and groans.

ORANG-UTAN
Pongo pygmaeus

Diet: mainly fruit, also shoots, insects, eggs, other small animals.

Breeding: 1 offspring after pregnancy of 8½-9 months.

Size: head-body 78cm, weight 40-50kg, height 115cm female; head-body 97cm, weight 60-90kg, height 137cm male.

Colour: orange-red, bright in the young, dark in adults. Face bare and black but pinkish on muzzle of young animals.

Lifespan: up to 35 years.

Habitat: tropical rain forest.

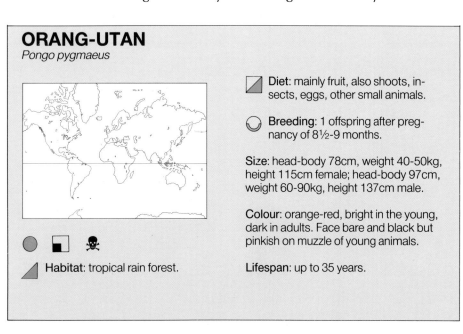

HIGH INTELLIGENCE

The orang-utan's ability to remember the location and fruiting times of individual trees in thick forest is one example of its high intelligence. In captivity these animals prove to be quick learners and good companions of humans.

In the wild, orang-utans have a very simple life-style and spend most of their time on their own. Males and females come together to mate, but when the female gets pregnant she goes off on her own to give birth and raise the baby. A male will usually maintain a relationship with several females in his territory. He makes his calls both to attract more females and to warn off other males.

Males usually try to avoid one another, and their long calls help them to keep their distance. If two males do meet, however, they kick up a rumpus, charging about, shaking and breaking off branches, calling and sometimes (though not often) fighting each other.

THREAT OF EXTINCTION

Orang-utans are shy, gentle creatures, and local people treat them with respect. Yet like the other "gentle apes", the gorillas, orang-utans are in danger of becoming extinct.

Once they were threatened by people who trapped them for export to zoos. But this has now mostly been stopped. Today, the greatest threat comes from the destruction of their rain forest habitat due to logging.

To improve the orang-utan's chances of survival, conservationists have set up nature reserves and national parks in Borneo and Sumatra and elsewhere in Indonesia and Malaysia.

▶The orang-utan spends most of its time in the trees. It swings on its long arms and takes hold of branches with its hook-like hands and feet.

GORILLA

Twice as big as the females around him, a mature "silverback" gorilla sits in the forest chewing a mouthful of leaves. Hearing a crashing in the undergrowth, he jumps to his feet. Advancing on him threateningly is a much younger "silverback". When they see each other they roar loudly, beating on their chests with both hands. The younger gorilla knows he's outclassed.

The gorilla is the largest of all the primates. Mature female gorillas are heavier than most human males. Mature males – known as silverbacks because of their silvery-white saddle – are twice as heavy again. Along with chimpanzees, gorillas are the most intelligent animals next to human beings.

Gorillas live in groups, usually of 5 to 10 animals. Each group is made up of one adult male and a number of females and their young.

GENTLE GIANTS

For most of the time, gorillas lead a peaceful life. They spend the greater part of the day feeding, since they need to eat a lot of food, mainly leaves, to maintain their huge bulk. In between they rest to allow plenty of time for digestion. At night they make platform nests of twigs and branches either on the ground or in low trees.

Gorillas spend more time on the ground than up in the trees. They occasionally walk on two feet, but for the most part they walk on all fours. Like chimpanzees, they walk on the soles of their feet and on the knuckles of the hands. Only young gorillas spend much time up in the trees.

Threat displays between rival gorillas can sometimes end in ferocious fights. The worst clashes occur between the silverback with a well-

▲An Eastern lowland gorilla eating a plant stem. Gorillas have large teeth and powerful jaws to crunch the huge amounts of leaves and stems they eat. Their jaws are worked by large muscles attached to a bony crest on the skull.

established "harem" and the lone young silverback. The loner tries to steal some or all of the other's females and set up a harem of his own.

In the wild gorillas do not feel threatened by human beings, and will allow them to approach quite close. But human visitors must stay quiet,

▼A silverback Mountain gorilla, leader of his "harem" of smaller females.

GORILLA *Gorilla gorilla*

● ■ ☠

◢ Habitat: tropical forest.

■ Diet: mostly leaves, some fruit.

◒ Breeding: 1 offspring after pregnancy of 8-9 months.

Size: height up to 180cm male, 150cm female; weight up to 180kg male, 90kg female.

Colour: coat black to brownish-grey.

Lifespan: up to 40 years.

Races mentioned in text:
Eastern lowland gorilla (*Gorilla gorilla graueri*)
Mountain gorilla (*G. g. beringei*)
Western lowland gorilla (*G. g. gorilla*)

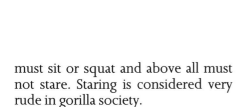

◄▼A gorilla group rests at midday after a morning's feeding. They gather, with the females and babies closest, around the silverback, the only mature male. One of the females grooms him. Older infants play together. Females with no offspring and maturing males stay on the edge of the group.

must sit or squat and above all must not stare. Staring is considered very rude in gorilla society.

SHRINKING HABITAT

The gorilla is a single species, but there are three separate races or sub-species. All are under threat, like so many other animals, from the destruction of their forest habitat. Hunting and trapping the young for sale to zoos are also reducing their numbers.

Most under threat is the Mountain gorilla, of which only about three or four hundred remain. The Mountain gorilla is found in Zaire, Rwanda and Uganda at altitudes between about 1,500m and 3,800m. A few thousand Eastern lowland gorilla remain, living in eastern Zaire. The Mountain and Eastern lowland gorillas have black coats. The male's silvery-white saddle is only on the back.

The Western lowland gorilla has a brownish tinge to its coat, and the male's saddle extends to the rump and thighs. It is found in Central West Africa from Cameroon to the Congo. About half of the total population (around 9,000) are concentrated in Gabon.

►A Mountain gorilla nursing her baby. She will feed it for up to three years and probably have another baby a year or so later. Gorillas make caring and affectionate mothers, but their babies do not always survive. In her lifetime a female gorilla may successfully raise only three or four offspring.

WOLVES

A long, piercing howl shatters the quiet of a northern forest. The howl grows into a chorus of many voices, and the forest valley soon echoes to the chilling sound. The leader of a wolf pack started this noise and other members joined in. The howling warns other wolf packs to keep away. There may be young cubs to protect or a kill to be guarded. For nearby farmers, the howling may mean that livestock become anxious and need to be calmed.

WOLVES Canidae (*2 species*)

   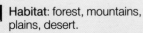

Habitat: forest, mountains, plains, desert.

Diet: berries, small mammals, caribou, deer, moose.

Breeding: litters of 4-7 after pregnancy of 61-63 days.

Size: head-body 100-150cm; weight 12-80kg; males larger than females.

Colour: grey to tawny-buff, varying from white in far north through red, brown to black; underside pale.

Lifespan: 8-16 years, up to 20 in captivity.

Species mentioned in text:
Domestic dog (*Canis familiaris*)
Grey wolf (*C. lupus*)
Red wolf (*C. rufus*)

▶**Wolves of the world** Red wolf (1). Arabian Grey wolf (2). Mexican Grey wolf (3). European Grey wolf (4). Tibetan Grey wolf (5). Grey wolf/husky cross (6).

Only two species of wolf survive today. The Grey wolf lives in the northern half of North America, Northern Europe and much of Asia. It is extinct in Britain and remains in Western Europe only in a few isolated areas. The decline of the Grey wolf is the result of the expansion of the human population, which led to the destruction of habitats. People have for centuries killed wolves, seeing them as a threat to farm animals. Our pet dogs are descended from wolves. The Red wolf once lived throughout south-east North America. It is now extinct in the wild except for a small group recently released in North Carolina.

LIFE IN THE PACK

Wolves are social animals and live in packs. A pack has 7 to 20 members, its size depending on the abundance of local prey. Wolves mate for life, so each pack consists of several pairs and their young.

Wolf packs have very large home ranges. The smallest is about 100sq km, while the largest may extend over 1,000sq km – the size depends on the amount of food available. Within each home range, a pack has its own territory which it guards against other

▼A wolf pack sets off in single file in search of prey. Their travels may cover an area up to 1,000sq km.

▲With lowered tail and flattened ears, a wolf greets the pack leader (1), while two cubs play (2).

packs. Wolves mark the boundaries of these areas by frequent scent-marking with urine and, less often, by howling. Wolf packs avoid each other as much as possible. When they do meet, there may be fights that result in deaths.

A strong, aggressive male leads each pack. His mate is the dominant female, and this leading pair breeds more often than the other pairs. A wolf signals its dominance by snarling and displaying its teeth, while other individuals show their acceptance of their lower position by holding their ears back and their tails between their legs. While an individual may be

lower in rank than the pack leader, it can also be dominant over other members of the pack.

BREEDING AND HUNTING

Wolves breed late in the winter. A female gives birth to a litter of between 4 and 7 blind, helpless cubs in a den. After about 4 weeks the cubs leave the den. They are looked after not only by their parents, but also by "helpers" among the other members of the pack.

By hunting together, a wolf pack can run down and kill animals which would be too big for a solitary wolf. They prey on deer, caribou and antelope, as well as smaller animals. Wolves also eat berries and scavenge at rubbish tips.

COYOTE

Pronghorn antelope graze quietly in the sagebrush country of western North America. Besides the strong scent of sagebrush, they now smell something else: danger. The danger is a pair of stalking coyotes. Pronghorns often approach moving objects, even predators. One does just that and pays for its curiosity with its life. The coyotes chase it for about 400m and kill it quickly – they have earned another meal.

The haunting howl of the coyote is commonly heard in cowboy films, where it is used to create a feeling of night-time menace. Coyotes live in almost all of North America and extend south through Mexico as far as Costa Rica. They are medium-sized, slender members of the dog family, with a narrow muzzle, pointed ears and long legs.

They inhabit open country, occasionally mountain forest. They prey on small animals, including insects, but especially rabbits, mice and ground squirrels. Coyotes also eat fruit, carrion and larger animals such as deer and pronghorn antelope. When stalking small prey, they hunt alone, but two or more coyotes stalk larger animals.

COYOTE PACKS

Until recently, coyotes were thought to be solitary animals, but we now know that they sometimes form packs and have social lives similar to wolves. A pack usually consists of about six adults, a few juveniles of about a year old and some young. Packs of this type form because the juveniles delay leaving to form pairs of their own. Instead, they stay with their family group as "helpers" and assist in rearing the younger cubs.

Packs probably form when there is a local abundance of prey. A pack has a

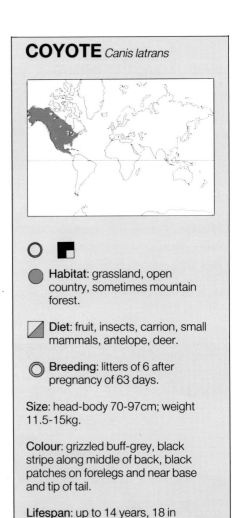

COYOTE *Canis latrans*

○ ■◱

◉ **Habitat:** grassland, open country, sometimes mountain forest.

◪ **Diet:** fruit, insects, carrion, small mammals, antelope, deer.

◎ **Breeding:** litters of 6 after pregnancy of 63 days.

Size: head-body 70-97cm; weight 11.5-15kg.

Colour: grizzled buff-grey, black stripe along middle of back, black patches on forelegs and near base and tip of tail.

Lifespan: up to 14 years, 18 in captivity.

home range of 14 to 65sq km, and pack members scent-mark the boundaries of the home range with urine. They also use their famous howl and other sounds to signal their presence.

PARENTAL CARE

Coyotes breed from January to March. Like wolves, they mate for life, and both parents share the rearing of young. A female produces one litter each year of about six blind, helpless pups. She suckles them in a den for several weeks, but at 3 weeks, they start to eat partly digested food brought to them and regurgitated by both parents and other members of the pack.

Unlike most carnivores, the coyote is not in decline. Since the late 19th century it has expanded its range northwards and eastwards across the United States. At the same time, the Grey Wolf and Red Wolf were being killed in huge numbers by human settlers.

▲A lone coyote pauses to sniff the air while out hunting in Banff National Park, Alberta, Canada.

◄Announcing its presence, a coyote produces its familiar howl, which can be heard several kilometres away.

▼An insect or small rodent has attracted the attention of this coyote, which follows it closely.

▲A coyote pack defends a kill. Three are feeding (1). The leader of the pack (2), his ears erect, tail bushy and almost horizontal and teeth exposed, threatens an intruder (3), who adopts a defensive threat posture, with tail between legs. Another male (4) backs up his dominant partner, while other intruders (5) await the outcome.

POLAR BEAR

A hole appears in a smooth bank of deep snow, high in the Arctic. Out of the hole peeps a black nose. The hole gets larger and the black nose is followed by a broad, massive white head. Eventually the huge bulk of a female Polar bear looms out of the hole and moves slowly down the bank. She stops and waits as two smaller heads appear at the hole. Her cubs blink at their first sight of the Sun as they leave the den where they were born.

Polar bears are the largest living four-legged carnivores. They survive in one of the harshest areas of the world, braving the freezing cold of the high Arctic. Much of their time is spent on the pack-ice, far from land.

Everything about Polar bears is geared for survival in extreme cold. They are well insulated by a thick fur coat and a layer of fat – only the nose and pads of the feet are without fur. Small ears and a very short tail also prevent the loss of body heat.

PATIENT HUNTERS

Polar bears are excellent swimmers and can swim for hours through icy-cold water. Their feet are slightly webbed, and each foot has five long, curved claws. The claws help them to grip not only the slippery ice but also their prey. And the white coat camouflages a Polar bear against the snow, allowing it to sneak up unnoticed on basking seals.

Polar bears mostly hunt seals, especially the Ringed seal. For most of the year they hunt by waiting patiently for seals to appear at their breathing-holes in the ice. In April and May they break into the dens of Ringed seals, killing the mothers and the pups.

Polar bears may even attack and kill small whales and walruses. They also

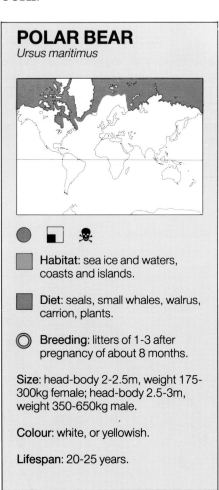

POLAR BEAR
Ursus maritimus

Habitat: sea ice and waters, coasts and islands.

Diet: seals, small whales, walrus, carrion, plants.

Breeding: litters of 1-3 after pregnancy of about 8 months.

Size: head-body 2-2.5m, weight 175-300kg female; head-body 2.5-3m, weight 350-650kg male.

Colour: white, or yellowish.

Lifespan: 20-25 years.

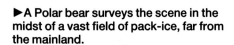

▶A Polar bear surveys the scene in the midst of a vast field of pack-ice, far from the mainland.

eat carrion and, in summer, some plant material. Polar bears are mostly solitary animals, though up to 30 may gather at a good food source such as a dead whale.

A male Polar bear finds a female on heat by following her smell. A single male may have a large home area which includes the home areas of several females. Breeding begins when Polar bears are 5 years old. They mate in April, May and June.

WINTER IN THE DEN
In November and December pregnant females dig dens in the snow. Each female remains in her den until March, and it is here that she gives birth to a litter of up to three cubs, each weighing 600 to 700g.

Polar-bear milk is about one-third fat, which helps the cubs to keep their body temperature up through the permanent night of the Arctic winter. Although the female Polar bear does not feed while she is in the den, she is not in true hibernation.

The cubs leave the den with their mother when they are about 3 months old and weigh 8 to 12kg.

▲A cub follows its mother across the ice. It will remain with her until it is about 28 months old.

▼Polar bears scavenge at a rubbish tip in Alaska. This happens when towns are built on bear migration routes.

GRIZZLY (BROWN) BEAR

It is spawning time for the Pacific salmon. As the large fish labour upstream along a Canadian river, a Grizzly bear and her cubs come tumbling down the bank into the shallows, where the salmon are leaping. With her claws and teeth, the female Grizzly catches fish after fish and neatly strips the flesh from both sides.

Grizzly bears are famous for their strength and speed. A Grizzly can bite through a steel bolt 12mm thick. Despite its lumbering weight of nearly half a tonne, it can charge at 50kph.

Grizzly bears are forest animals and today are found in north-west North America and Europe and northern Asia. They are often called Brown bears and are rare, with only a few small isolated populations remaining.

Grizzlies eat mainly plants, especially young leaves and berries – they use their strong claws to dig up tubers and roots. They also eat insect grubs, rats and mice, salmon, trout and young deer. Sometimes Grizzlies will attack farm animals.

SPRING COURTSHIP

Male Grizzlies are solitary animals. Each adult male has a home range of up to 1,000sq km, which he defends fiercely against other males. They often fight to the death. Females also have territories, which they may share with a few young daughters. Their territories are smaller than those of males, up to 190sq km. Females, too, defend their territories against other females, so that they can enjoy exclusive access to food.

In spring, male Grizzlies seek out females. After a short courtship of 2 to 15 days they mate in May and June. As with all bears, the fertilized egg does not implant in the womb until October or November. At this time, the

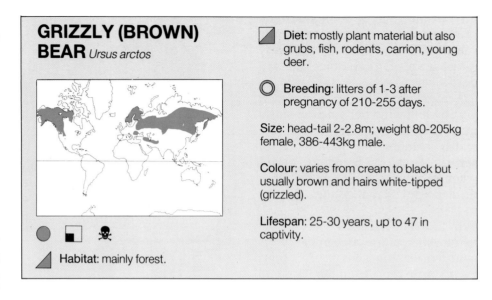

GRIZZLY (BROWN) BEAR *Ursus arctos*

● ■ ☠

△ Habitat: mainly forest.

▨ Diet: mostly plant material but also grubs, fish, rodents, carrion, young deer.

◯ Breeding: litters of 1-3 after pregnancy of 210-255 days.

Size: head-tail 2-2.8m; weight 80-205kg female, 386-443kg male.

Colour: varies from cream to black but usually brown and hairs white-tipped (grizzled).

Lifespan: 25-30 years, up to 47 in captivity.

female either digs out her own den or finds a natural cave or a hollow tree. She remains there throughout the winter, not feeding, but relying on her store of body fat.

She gives birth to two or three naked, helpless cubs, each weighing only 350 to 400g. They remain in the den until April, May or June and stay with their mother for up to about 4½ years.

FEW SAFE AREAS

Grizzlies are now endangered in many parts of North America. They are sometimes shot when they feed at rubbish tips and have been wiped out in many areas.

Despite their fierce reputation, Grizzlies rarely attack people. When a bear does attack, it is sometimes because with its poor eyesight it mistakes a person for another bear.

▼ Grizzlies love water and spend much time in and around salmon rivers bathing, frolicking and feeding.

► A bear hug: two young male Grizzlies in a play fight, which is good practice for adult fighting.

RACCOONS

Late in the evening, at the edge of a marsh sits a raccoon. It reaches down with its hands to feel and grope in the water among the mud and plant roots. The raccoon does not seem to watch what its hands are doing. Suddenly it pulls out a hand, grasping a small frog. Dunking its catch back in the water, it washes the frog backwards and forwards, before finally eating it.

Raccoons are American relatives of the pandas of south-east Asia. Four species are each found on a single island. Two species are widespread.

The Common raccoon lives as far north as southern Canada and as far south as Central America. The Crab-eating raccoon is found in Central America and northern South America. Raccoons eat a wide range of foods, foraging in trees, on the ground and also in water.

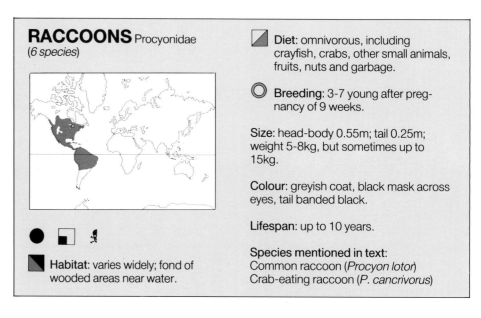

RACCOONS Procyonidae
(6 species)

● ■ ☠

Habitat: varies widely; fond of wooded areas near water.

Diet: omnivorous, including crayfish, crabs, other small animals, fruits, nuts and garbage.

Breeding: 3-7 young after pregnancy of 9 weeks.

Size: head-body 0.55m; tail 0.25m; weight 5-8kg, but sometimes up to 15kg.

Colour: greyish coat, black mask across eyes, tail banded black.

Lifespan: up to 10 years.

Species mentioned in text:
Common raccoon (*Procyon lotor*)
Crab-eating raccoon (*P. cancrivorus*)

MOBILE HANDS

A raccoon's hands are very mobile and have a good sense of touch. It uses them to explore food, especially in water. This behaviour is so ingrained that a raccoon in captivity may take food, place it in water, and then retrieve it. This has led to the myth that raccoons "wash" their food.

LIVING WITH PEOPLE

Raccoons are fond of crayfish, but they will eat foods ranging from mice and worms to birds and their eggs. They also eat fruit and corn and sometimes raid crops, which makes them unpopular with farmers. They are curious and will investigate all kinds of places and sources of food.

▲The Crab-eating raccoon is a good climber and has a long tail. It also spends time in and near water.

▶A Common raccoon rests at the entrance to its den. Raccoons are active mostly during the night.

Raccoons sometimes make dens in barns and sheds, living close to people and making a living on their left-overs. This is probably one reason why the Common raccoon has been able to spread northwards in recent years. Unfortunately, it is an important carrier of the disease rabies, so its presence is not always welcome.

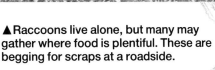

▲ Raccoons live alone, but many may gather where food is plentiful. These are begging for scraps at a roadside.

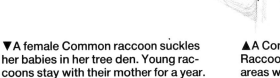

▼ A female Common raccoon suckles her babies in her tree den. Young raccoons stay with their mother for a year.

▲ A Common raccoon raids a dustbin. Raccoons have learned to live even in areas where there are many humans.

WINTER DENS

In the northern part of its range the Common raccoon puts on fat in autumn. It stays in a den for much of the winter, although it does not truly hibernate. Dens may be in hollow trees or below ground. A family of raccoons may den together, even though the young go their own way to find food. As many as 23 raccoons have been found squeezed together in a winter den.

Common raccoons are born in the spring. A mother produces her litter in the security of a tree den. The young are tiny and undeveloped, only about 70g in weight. It is 7 weeks or more before they are able to leave the den unaided, and not till 10 weeks old do they follow their mother.

Raccoons begin to breed when they are 1 or 2 years old. Males grow rather bigger than females.

PANDAS

A Giant panda pushes its way through the bamboo forest with a rolling walk. It is seeking the spot it found yesterday where tender new bamboo shoots were sprouting. It comes to the clearing it remembers, but the place is already occupied. Another panda is sitting there, chewing on the bamboo. The new arrival mutters a few growls, then sits in the clearing far from the other panda. It turns its back and starts to feed.

▶The Giant panda looks very human as it sits with its body upright and puts food to its mouth with its front paws.

▼As well as five toes, the Giant and the Red panda have an enlarged wrist bone that can be folded over to work as a "thumb". In this way pandas can grasp the bamboo shoots that they love to eat.

▼Giant pandas look like bears, which genetic evidence shows are their closest relatives.

PANDAS Procyonidae
(*2 species*)

▲ Habitat: mountain forest.

◢ Diet: bamboo shoots, grasses, bulbs, fruits, some insects, rodents and carrion.

○ **Breeding**: 1 or 2 cubs after pregnancy of 125-150 days (Giant panda); 1-4 young after pregnancy of 90-145 days (Red panda).

Size: Red panda: head-body 0.5-0.6m plus 40cm tail, weight 3-5kg; Giant panda: head-body 1.2-1.5m plus 12cm tail, weight 100-150kg.

Colour: black and white (Giant panda); reddish chestnut, black below, light markings on face (Red panda).

Lifespan: 14-20 years.

Species mentioned in text:
Giant panda (*Ailuropoda melanoleuca*)
Red panda (*Ailurus fulgens*)

There are two species of panda. The Giant panda is black and white and bear-like. It lives in central and western China. The Lesser or Red panda has a beautiful reddish-chestnut back, darker below and on the legs, and lighter face markings. It is shaped like a chubby cat and has a long tail. It is found from Nepal to western China in mountain forests.

The Red panda was known to Western scientists a long time before the Giant panda was discovered in 1869. The Red panda finds most of its food in trees. It eats bamboo, fruit, acorns, lichens, roots and some small animals. Like the Giant panda it has an extra wrist bone that can be used as a thumb, though not so well. It is nocturnal and lives a solitary life.

BAMBOO DIET

The Giant panda, like the Red panda, belongs to the group of mammals called the Carnivores. Most of its relations, such as lions and wolves, eat meat most of the time, but the Giant panda has adapted to a life of feeding mainly on bamboo. It feeds on both the shoots and the roots but, whenever available, it prefers the leaves and slender stems. The Giant panda's cheek teeth are specialized for slicing and crushing food, and it can cope with stems up to about 40mm in diameter. It also eats some bulbs and tubers of other plants, grasses and some small animals.

Although bamboo forms the main part of its diet, the Giant panda's gut is not especially efficient at digesting it, and much of the bamboo passes straight through the body. To get enough nourishment the Giant panda may spend as much as 12 hours a day feeding.

MATING AND RAISING YOUNG

The Giant panda is largely solitary in the wild. There are scent glands beneath its tail, and it rubs these against large objects in the surround-

▲ The Red panda has big whiskers. With its long tail, short legs and sharp claws it is well built for climbing.

ings. This probably marks the territory and keeps away other pandas of the same sex. Even males and females are little interested in one another except in the brief mating season in the spring. Male and female find one another by scent and sound. After a brief mating they separate again.

A pair of cubs, sometimes three, are born in a sheltered den. Normally only one survives. Cubs are small, blind and helpless, weighing only about 100g. Their eyes do not open for 6 or 7 weeks, and the cub cannot follow its mother until it is about 3 months old. It is weaned at 6 months. At a year old it may move off to live independently. Female Giant pandas are able to reproduce when about 4 or 5 years old, but the males are probably

not fully mature until about 6 or 7 years old. Full-grown males are about 10 per cent larger and 20 per cent heavier than females.

PANDA PROBLEMS

The Giant panda is a rare animal. Fewer than 1,000 survive in the wild. It has probably always been a rare animal, because its way of life confines it to a limited area – bamboo forests at heights of 2,600 to 3,500m. Although it is protected and lives in remote areas, its populations are so small that it is likely to die out.

One of the panda's chief foods is a bamboo which flowers only about every 100 years and then dies back. This has happened recently in some parts of the panda's range, and some pandas may have starved as a result. Yet as a species the Giant panda must have survived these flowerings many times before and can do so again.

SKUNKS

A female Striped skunk is out on a night's foraging. She has dug some beetles from the soft earth. Now she is at the edge of a wood, listening and waiting for the chance to catch a young rabbit. Another animal, a fox, steals along the edge of the wood. The skunk does not run away from it. She stamps in annoyance and walks stiff-legged in the moonlight. She is easy to see, holding her bushy tail straight up. The fox hesitates, then quickly goes past, keeping well clear of the skunk.

SKUNKS Mustelidae; sub-family Mephitinae (*13 species*)

Diet: insects, small mammals, eggs, some fruit.

Breeding: 2-9 young after pregnancy of 42-66 days.

Size: head-tail 40-70cm; weight 0.5-3kg.

Colour: mainly black, with white stripes or spots.

Lifespan: up to 10 years.

Species mentioned in text:
Hooded skunk (*Mephitis macroura*)
Pygmy spotted skunk (*Spilogale pygmaea*)
Striped skunk (*Mephitis mephitis*)

Habitat: woods, open country, desert.

All species of skunk live in North, Central or South America. There are three main types. Seven species of hog-nosed skunk live in the southern USA, Central and South America. They have a long bare muzzle and large claws, which are both adaptations to digging.

The four spotted skunks live in the USA and Central America. They are light in build and are good climbers. Spotted skunks are striped, but these stripes may be broken into spots. The Striped skunk is a common species in North America and northern Mexico. The Hooded skunk is found in the south-west USA.

MAKING A STINK

The weasel family all have anal scent glands, but these are best developed in the skunks. Skunks are able to spray the contents of the two glands in the direction of an enemy. The spray is aimed at the face and causes intense irritation of the skin – sometimes even temporary blindness.

The spray is accurate over 2m or more. It contains sulphur compounds with an unbearable and very clinging smell. Although this is a good deterrent against most enemies, Great horned owls still attack skunks. Other animals may also attack if desperate with hunger. But usually a skunk is safe and not afraid of these predators. Skunks and their dens do not smell of the powerful spray.

THREAT DISPLAYS

Skunks do not hide from enemies. Instead they put on a warning display.

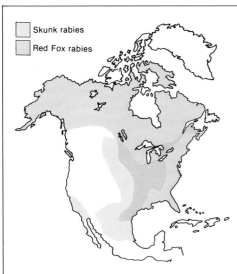

Skunk rabies

Red Fox rabies

◀Skunks are common carriers of the disease rabies in the USA. Infected skunks have the rabies virus in their saliva and tend to bite almost anything that moves. The map shows where rabies occurs in skunks and Red foxes in North America.

▶ Most animals avoid a skunk that gives a threat display or sprays. Rabid foxes, though, may still attack it, so infecting the skunk and spreading the disease.

Together with their obvious black and white colour this is usually enough to put off an enemy. Only as a last resort does the skunk shoot its stinking spray.

The ability to spray scent develops at only a month old. When a skunk is born it is blind and hairless, but even then the skin shows signs of the pattern that will develop in the fur. The Striped skunk's eyes open at about 3 weeks, by which time the fur has grown. At 5 weeks the young begin to move around with the mother, finishing suckling at about 2 months. By the autumn after their birth (usually in May) the young are looking after themselves.

▲The Pygmy spotted skunk is a rare species found only on the Pacific coast of Mexico. Spotted skunks have silky fur.

Skunks are found in many habitats, including towns. They are basically meat-eaters, but consume almost any food. They rest up in dens in bad weather. Skunks suffer from fleas, ticks and flatworms and from diseases such as rabies and distemper.

▼**Species of skunk** A Western spotted skunk (*Spilogale gracilis*) **(1)** does a handstand, a threat made before spraying its scent. The Hooded skunk **(2)** of the south-west USA. The Hog-nosed skunk (*Conepatus mesoleucus*) **(3)** has a long bare snout. In the very common Striped skunk**(4, 5)** the white stripes vary in number and thickness.

OTTERS

Off the Californian coast a Sea otter dives to the sea bed. It digs out a clam and a stone, then returns to the surface. The otter lies on its back at the surface balancing the stone on its chest. Taking the clam in one hand, it bangs it down repeatedly on the stone. The clam shell cracks, and the otter feeds on the flesh inside. Then it washes off the remains by rolling over. The stone stays in the otter's hands, to be used again.

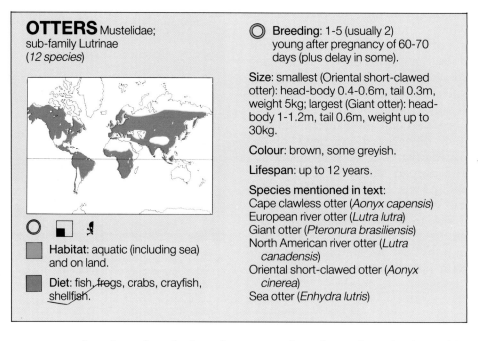

OTTERS Mustelidae; sub-family Lutrinae (*12 species*)

○ ■□ 🦦

Habitat: aquatic (including sea) and on land.

Diet: fish, frogs, crabs, crayfish, shellfish.

○ Breeding: 1-5 (usually 2) young after pregnancy of 60-70 days (plus delay in some).

Size: smallest (Oriental short-clawed otter): head-body 0.4-0.6m, tail 0.3m, weight 5kg; largest (Giant otter): head-body 1-1.2m, tail 0.6m, weight up to 30kg.

Colour: brown, some greyish.

Lifespan: up to 12 years.

Species mentioned in text:
Cape clawless otter (*Aonyx capensis*)
European river otter (*Lutra lutra*)
Giant otter (*Pteronura brasiliensis*)
North American river otter (*Lutra canadensis*)
Oriental short-clawed otter (*Aonyx cinerea*)
Sea otter (*Enhydra lutris*)

As well as the Sea otter of the North Pacific there are another 11 species of otter found across most continents except Australasia and Antarctica. Several species venture into the sea, but most prefer the rivers, lakes and marshes. Otters can move across country, but like to be near water, where they find food.

HUNTING SESSIONS
Otters have tight-packed underfur with long guard hairs. The coat repels water and soon dries. An otter's body is very supple. The tail is thick and muscular at the base, flattened below and in some species flattened above too. It helps in swimming. Most kinds of otter have webbed paws.

Otters are active and energetic. Many species have several hunting sessions in a day. An otter may eat daily 1kg of food spread over several meals. The teeth are very strong, helping otters crush the bones of their prey. They digest their food quickly, giving them boundless energy.

MANY VOICES
Most otters, such as the European and North American river otters, live singly except when breeding. Then a

▼An Oriental short-clawed otter shows its streamlined shape under water, when its ears and nostrils are closed.

▲ The Cape clawless otter uses its hands to catch and eat prey. Its long whiskers help it sense moving prey.

pair may stay together for just a few months. Other otters, such as the Cape clawless otter, live in pairs all the time. The most social otters include the Giant otter and the Oriental short-clawed otter. These move around in larger groups based on families.

Otters make many sounds. They chirp or bark to keep in touch and make a chattering sound when close. They also growl. Another way otters communicate is by scent. They may deposit droppings, urine or scent from the anal glands. These scents mark out territories and give information to other otters about the animal that left them. Groups of Giant otters in Brazil make communal scent areas on river banks, clearing all the plants in a wide semicircle.

▶ Clever hands The Oriental short-clawed otter (1, forepaw a) catches prey with its hands and is good at feeling and grasping, as is the Cape clawless otter (b). The Spot-necked otter (*Hydrictis maculicollis*) (2) has webbed fingers (e) and catches food with its mouth. So does the Giant otter (c). The Indian smooth- coated otter (*Lutrogale perspicillata*) (3), has webbed fingers (d) but can hold a shell to its mouth. North American river otter (4,f) has a bare nose. Species can be told apart (i-viii) by the nose's shape.

CIVETS

At night, in the humid rain forests of West Africa, there is a constant babble of noise. But every now and then, this wall of noise is interrupted by a loud, ghostly cry, like the hooting of an owl. Similar cries reply from a kilometre away. These are African palm civets calling to one another.

Civets and their relatives, the genets and linsangs, are cat-like mammals. Most live in the hot, moist areas of Africa or Asia, though one kind, the Common genet, lives in southern France, Spain and Portugal. They are animals of the night, so have large eyes. They also have a good sense of smell and excellent hearing. Long tails enable them to keep their balance when climbing trees. They live mainly in forests, and eat insects, small mammals and fruit. The Bear cat or binturong of South-east Asia has a powerful, long tail which it uses to hang on to branches.

There are eight species of palm civet, one in Africa and seven in Asia. They all spend most of their time in trees, where they are skilled climbers, gaining grip with strong, curved claws. Palm civets eat many kinds of fruit,

even some which are poisonous to humans. The Common palm civet of Asia eats the fruit of at least 35 types of plant. Like all the other palm civets, it also eats snails, scorpions, birds, rats and mice. This species is very common, often living close to people, and in some areas it is a pest.

On the other hand, the Otter civet and Jerdon's palm civet, both from Asia, and the Large spotted civet, from South Africa, are now all very rare and endangered species.

A WORLD OF SMELLS
A male palm civet has a special home area or territory which he patrols regularly. He marks the edge of his area with a scent made in a fold of skin at his rear end. People collect the scent from captive animals for use in expensive perfumes. A strong, healthy male may have one to three females in a large home area. He visits the females' own areas every few days.

THE PERFECT KILLER
Genets feed on insects, lizards, small birds, rats and mice. They have sharp teeth and excellent sight. They live mainly in trees, but also hunt on the ground. Genets are such good hunters that in Europe the Common genet was once kept as a rat-catcher.

▲ A Giant or Celebes palm civet eating a young shoot. This rarely seen civet lives only on the island of Sulawesi (Celebes).

► Types of civet An African linsang (*Poiana richarsoni*) (1) eats a nestling bird. The Banded palm civet (*Hemigalus derbyanua*) (2) devours a lizard, while an Oriental civet (*Viverra tangaluna*) (3) smells an enemy and raises its crest of bristly hairs. An ever-curious Common palm civet (4) sniffs the air for signs of a mate. Using its tail for support, a Bear cat or binturong (5) searches for fruit.

CIVETS Viverridae *(35 species)*

◢ Habitat: mainly in trees in forests, scrub, mountains; also along river banks.

◰ Diet: varied, including fruit, leaves, shoots, insects, small lizards, frogs, birds, rats, mice.

◯ Breeding: litter of 1-3 after pregnancy of 70-90 days.

Size: smallest (African linsang): head-tail 71cm, weight 0.65kg; largest (African civet): head-tail 126cm, weight 13kg.

Colour: dark spots and/or banding on a pale, sandy background.

Lifespan: 15-34 years.

Species mentioned in text:
African civet (*Civettictis civetta*)
African palm civet (*Nandinia binotata*)
Bear cat or binturong (*Arctictis binturong*)
Common genet (*Genetta genetta*)
Common palm civet (*Paradoxurus hermaphroditus*)
Giant or Celebes palm civet (*Macrogalidia musschebroekii*)
Jerdon's palm civet (*Paradoxurus jerdoni*)
Large spotted civet (*Viverra megaspila*)
Otter civet (*Cynogale bennettii*)

● ▢ ⚘

MONGOOSES

At dawn a pack of 14 Banded mongooses leave their termite-mound den. They move off in single file, then fan out to search for beetles. They keep in contact by calling to one another. An adult has stayed in the den to guard the group's 10 babies. Hours later the pack returns. Mothers suckle babies, while several younger adults bring them beetles. Then the main pack sets off after food again.

MONGOOSES Viverridae; sub-families Herpestinae, Galidiinae (*31 species*)

○ **Breeding:** 2-4 young after pregnancy of 42-105 days.

Size: smallest (Dwarf mongoose): head-body 24cm, tail 19cm, weight 0.3kg; largest (White-tailed mongoose):head-body 58cm, tail 44cm, weight 5kg.

Colour: brown to yellowish, grizzled or brindled harsh fur.

Lifespan: 10 years.

Species mentioned in text:
Banded mongoose (*Mungos mungo*)
Small Indian mongoose (*Herpestes javanicus*)
Suricate or Grey meercat (*Suricata suricatta*)

● ■

■ **Habitat:** forest, woodland, savannah, desert.
■ **Diet:** small mammals, reptiles, insects, some fruits.

Twenty species of mongoose are African. Four more live in Madagascar. Seven species live in South Asia. They are often the commonest carnivores in the places they live. Agile and active, some climb, but most species live on the ground.

SNAKE KILLERS?

Mongooses are famous for killing snakes and some really do kill venomous snakes. Mongooses are fast and alert, and tire less quickly than a reptile. They dodge the snake's fangs until they can jump in with a killing bite to the neck.

But most mongooses feed on easier prey, taking a whole range of small

◄Suricates scan their surroundings in the Kalahari desert. These mongooses live in groups and are active by day.

▼**Mongoose species** Adult Dwarf mongoose (*Helogale parvula*) (**1**) feeding a youngster. Selous' mongoose (*Paracynictis selousi*) (**2**). Narrow-striped mongoose (*Mungotictis decemlineata*) (**3**). Egyptian mongoose (*Herpestes ichneumon*) (**4**) about to break an egg on a rock. Marsh mongoose (*Atilax pauludinosus*) (**5**) scent-marks a stone.

White-tailed mongoose (*Ichneumia albicauda*) (**6**). Ring-tailed mongoose (*Galidia elegans*) (**7**).

▶Banded mongooses work together as a pack when feeding. As a group they can repel large enemies like jackals.

animals. Some kinds are especially fond of insects. Others eat crabs and frogs. Many mongooses can crack open eggs by throwing them against stones before lapping up the very nutritious contents.

MONGOOSE GROUPS

Most mongooses live by themselves or sometimes in pairs. Most hunt stealthily by night. A few species such as the Banded mongoose live in close-knit groups and are active by day. Group members defend each other from attacks by predators.

The Small Indian mongoose was introduced to Hawaii and the West Indies in the hope it would kill rodent pests. Unfortunately it killed many native animals too and is now thought of as a pest itself.

CHEETAH

A female cheetah sits on top of a termite mound in Africa, while her three cubs frolic below. For the moment, she is content to let them play. But she will soon carry on teaching the cubs how to hunt and kill prey. They will follow her white-tipped tail through the long grass, stopping at her command before she chases down a gazelle. Then she will call them to the prey. While she holds it down, they will practise the killing bite.

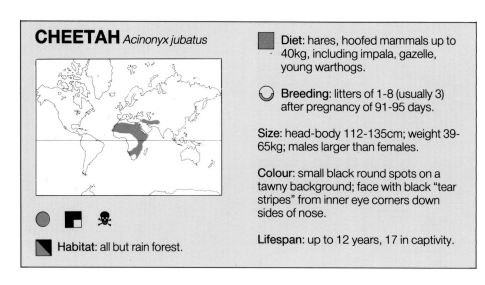

CHEETAH *Acinonyx jubatus*

Diet: hares, hoofed mammals up to 40kg, including impala, gazelle, young warthogs.

Breeding: litters of 1-8 (usually 3) after pregnancy of 91-95 days.

Size: head-body 112-135cm; weight 39-65kg; males larger than females.

Colour: small black round spots on a tawny background; face with black "tear stripes" from inner eye corners down sides of nose.

Lifespan: up to 12 years, 17 in captivity.

Habitat: all but rain forest.

▲Powered by long, muscular hind legs, a cheetah sprints at 96kph. A flexible spine allows it to make very long strides. The claws, even when held back, are not covered by a sheath but exposed, giving it a better grip on the ground.

▼With the acceleration of a high-powered sports car, a cheetah breaks cover to chase a Thomson's gazelle. An average chase covers 170m and lasts less than a minute. About half of these chases end with a successful kill.

With its small head and slim, loose-limbed build, the cheetah is the most distinctive of the big, spotted cats. Once common over much of Africa and the Middle East, only about 25,000 now survive in Africa.

FASTEST ON EARTH

The cheetah is best known as the fastest animal on Earth, capable of speeds up to 96kph. This skill is put to good use when it pursues hares and its more normal range of prey species, which include impala and gazelles.

Every year in Africa, the female cheetah follows the migration of its

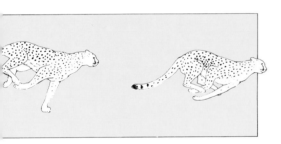

prey animals, moving through a home range of up to 800 sq km. The female is not territorial, so the home ranges of two or more females may overlap.

The male cheetah is aggressive. He will fight other males, sometimes to the death, in defence of his territory. Males usually live in groups, remaining together for life and marking their territories by spraying urine at regular intervals on landmarks such as tree stumps. Males also hunt together.

The cheetah breeds all the year round. The male does not help with rearing the young. At birth the cubs weigh 250 to 300g, and their eyes open at 2 to 11 days. When a few weeks old,

◄Alerted by the presence of prey, a female cheetah leaves cover and is about to begin stalking.

they leave their hiding-place and follow the mother around, eating some of the prey she catches. She weans them at about 3 months, but they remain with her until they are 17 to 23 months old, when female offspring leave one by one. The young males leave as a group – they are usually chased away from the area by older, more experienced males.

SECRETS OF SUCCESS

The cheetah shares the same areas as lions, leopards and hyenas. Its legendary speed helps it survive in this fierce competition. The cheetah also tends to hunt around the middle of the day, when the other large animals are usually asleep.

Daytime hunting, though, has its disadvantages. Vultures may drive a cheetah away from its kill and, at the same time, attract the attention of other hunters, which may then steal the prey. The cheetah avoids this by taking the kill to a hiding-place.

▼A strangling bite to the throat has killed this Thomson's gazelle. The cheetah now drags it to cover.

TRUE SEALS

Smooth sleek bodies bask on the shore in the golden sunlight of late afternoon, their mottled fur blending with the rocks. They are Grey seals. Sometimes one of them rolls over and lazily strokes its belly with a flipper. In the swirling sea near by a round grey head with large dark eyes scans the scene before diving out of sight. Below the waves the supple bodies of more Grey seals twist and turn as they chase fish for supper. Exhausted, other Grey seals haul themselves out of the spray to join their sunbathing companions.

Seals are sleek, plump mammals that live in polar and temperate seas and oceans. They are graceful swimmers with short stubby flippers. Their bodies glide easily through the water as they swim. Seals' foreflippers are modified wrists and hands, their hind flippers ankles and feet.

EARLESS SEALS
True seals have no external ear-flaps, and this marks them out from sea lions and fur seals, their close rel-

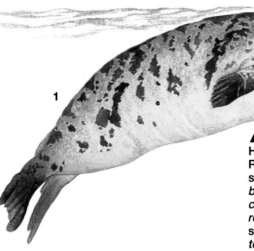

▲ ▶ **Northern and southern true seals**
Hooded seal (*Cystophora cristata*) (1). Ringed seal (2). Grey seal (3). Harp seal (4). Bearded seal (*Erignathus barbatus*) (5). Ribbon seal (*Phoca fasciata*) (6). Ross seal (*Ommatophoca rossi*) (7). Weddell seal (8). Crabeater seal (9). Leopard seal (*Hydrurga leptonyx*) (10). Southern elephant seal (11). Hawaiian monk seal (*Monachus schauinslandi*) (12).

▼ Harp seals look out for danger in the Canadian pack ice.

TRUE SEALS Phocidae
(*19 species*)

Habitat: offshore rocks and islands, pack-ice, land-fast ice, some large lakes.

Diet: prawns, squid, fish and (larger species of seals) sea-birds and smaller seals.

Breeding: usually 1 young after pregnancy of 10-11 months.

Size: smallest (Ringed seal): head-tail 117cm, weight 45kg; largest (Southern elephant seal): head-tail 490cm, weight 2,400kg; sexes usually the same size, but males of some species and females of others are much larger.

Colour: shades of grey or brown, often with dark spots or patches; young of some species white or tan at birth.

Lifespan: up to 56 years.

Species mentioned in text:
Crabeater seal (*Lobodon carcinophagus*)
Grey seal (*Halichoerus grypus*)
Harbour seal (*Phoca vitulina*)
Harp seal (*P. groenlandica*)
Northern elephant seal (*Mirounga angustirostris*)
Ringed seal (*Phoca hispida*)
Southern elephant seal (*Mirounga leonina*)
Weddell seal (*Leptonychotes weddelli*)

atives. True seals' flippers are weak and they cannot raise their bodies off the ground when on land. A true seal moves on land by using first its chest and then its belly to take its weight.

True seals are more powerful swimmers than sea lions. They use their hind flippers to propel themselves through the water, swinging the back end of their body from side to side.

UNDERWATER HUNTERS

Seals are underwater hunters. They feed on fish, shrimps, squid and sea-birds, which they catch with their pointed teeth. Their large eyes help them see in the dim underwater world.

Sea water is cool, especially at depth, and seals have a thick layer of fat (called blubber) under the skin which prevents them losing heat too quickly. It also helps to give them their smooth shape. The Weddell seal, like other seals, is a good diver, able to go 600m below the surface. It can close its nostrils and hold its breath for more than an hour.

THE SEAL YEAR

Seals breed slowly. The females are not usually ready to breed until they are at least 3 or 4 years old, and they produce only one pup at a time. Seals have to come on to land to give birth, usually in spring or early summer. New-born seals have soft and warm fur, which is not very waterproof.

Female seals (cows) produce some of the richest milk known. In just a few weeks a baby Crabeater seal can grow from 25kg to 120kg feeding only on its mother's milk. Suckling may last from 10 days to 12 weeks. Then the cow is ready to mate again.

Male true seals (bulls) often mate with more than one cow. Elephant seals and the Grey seal gather in large numbers on beaches to breed. Each bull defends his own patch of beach and his cows. The bulls roar and slash at each other with their teeth. Weddell seals, Ringed seals and Harbour seals defend underwater territories instead.

After mating, the seals return to the sea to feed. The females are now pregnant, but the babies inside them will not start to develop for 2½ to 3½ months.

►A pregnant Ringed seal digs out a snow cave above a crack in the pack-ice (inset). Here she will give birth. In this cave, the mother and her pup will be hidden from enemies like the Polar bear and Arctic fox. The snow above will help to keep out the cold.

►The huge nose of the male Northern elephant seal can be inflated to impress a rival. On his neck are rolls of blubber which may be up to 10cm thick.

STILL IN DANGER

In the past, seals have been killed on a large scale for their fur, skins, meat and blubber. Today, international laws limit the numbers that can be killed, and some species are completely protected. But the monk seals are still in danger of becoming extinct, especially in the Mediterranean. This is mainly because the warm coasts where they live are much disturbed by tourists, fishermen and divers.

▼This may look like a family group, but the male Crabeater seal is not the pup's father. He is waiting to mate with its mother.

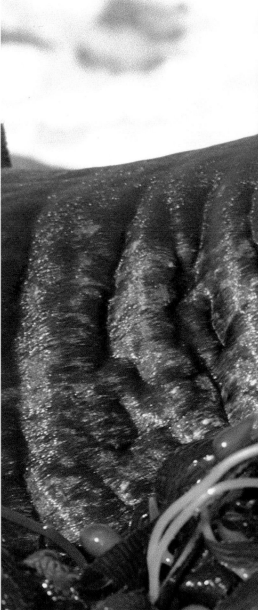

WALRUS

With a grunt and a splash the large bristly snout of a walrus comes out of the water. It is followed by 1,000kg of brownish-pink flesh. Using his long pointed tusks as levers, the walrus hauls himself out of the sea on to an ice-floe. He shuffles towards a group of dozing walruses and flops down on the ice to snooze, using the belly of another walrus as a pillow.

The walrus is rather like a giant pink sea lion. It has flippers instead of legs, and a fat spindle-shaped body. It is a powerful swimmer and can stay at sea for up to 2 days at a time. When on land, the walrus props up its body on its foreflippers, tucking its hind flippers underneath. It walks awkwardly, shuffling along on its flippers.

The females (cows) and young males have short velvety coats. Adult males (bulls) have little hair and look naked. Their skin is up to 5cm thick, wrinkled like an old leather bag.

The walrus has such a short thick neck that its head seems to be joined directly to its shoulders. Its squarish snout is covered in stiff bristles. One pair of teeth in the upper jaws of both sexes form tusks up to 55cm long.

WHY HAVE TUSKS?

The walrus does not use its tusks for feeding. It feeds on the sea bed, using the bristles on its snout to feel for clams, mussels and other sea creatures. It digs in the mud with its snout, which is covered in extra tough skin. Sometimes it shoots a jet of water from its mouth to blast prey animals out of their burrows.

The walrus uses its tusks like ice-axes to haul itself on to ice-floes, or to smash breathing-holes in the ice.

A walrus also uses its tusks to establish its place in the group. Walruses usually live in very large groups, sometimes of several thousand animals, and there are often arguments. The male walruses with the largest tusks get the best places on the ice or beach and the best chance of mating with the females. Walruses display to each other, showing off their tusks. If a display does not settle a dispute, the walruses may stab at each other with their tusks.

For thousands of years, Eskimos have hunted walruses for their skins and meat. Where stocks allow, this continues today.

►Sunbathing walruses look pink as their blood flows to the surface to absorb the Sun's warmth. The walrus just leaving the water is much paler, its blood flowing deeper to avoid losing heat to the cold water.

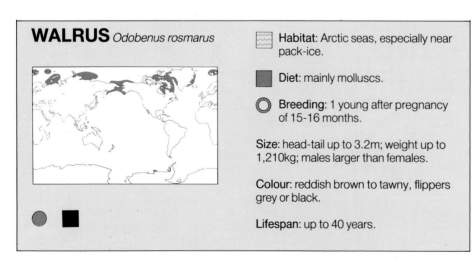

WALRUS *Odobenus rosmarus*

≋ **Habitat:** Arctic seas, especially near pack-ice.

■ **Diet:** mainly molluscs.

◯ **Breeding:** 1 young after pregnancy of 15-16 months.

Size: head-tail up to 3.2m; weight up to 1,210kg; males larger than females.

Colour: reddish brown to tawny, flippers grey or black.

Lifespan: up to 40 years.

GREY WHALE

With a flick of its huge tail, the Grey whale power-dives its way down to the sea bed. There it swims along the bottom, its head ploughing through the thick layer of sediment. It scoops up a mouthful of crustaceans, worms and muddy water and returns to the surface. On the surface it expels the muddy water through its plates of baleen and swallows the food filtered out. Then it dives again.

▼Grey whale mother and calf. The calf is especially sleek and smooth-skinned.

GREY WHALE *Eschrichtius robustus*

◼ **Diet:** bottom-dwelling marine animals, such as crustaceans and worms.

◯ **Breeding:** 1 offspring after pregnancy of about 13 months.

Size: head-tail 11.9-14.3m, weight 16 tonnes male; head-tail 12.8-15.2m, weight (pregnant) up to 34 tonnes female.

Colour: mottled grey.

Lifespan: up to 77 years.

◯ ◼ ☠

▦ **Habitat:** mainly coastal waters.

◀Large clusters of barnacles cover much of the Grey whale's skin as it gets older. Pale spidery whale lice live in the barnacle clusters.

▲The Grey whale blows as it comes up to the surface for air (**1**). Soon it dives again (**2**). Sometimes it "spy-hops" to get its bearings (**3**).

The Grey whale is one of the baleen whales. These whales feed on small sea creatures, which they catch by straining mouthfuls of sea water through horny plates called baleen (whalebone). The Grey whale's baleen is much shorter and stiffer than that of the other baleen whales, such as the Blue and Right whales. Like all the whales, it is a mammal whose young are, from birth, raised on the mother's milk.

There are two main populations of Grey whales, which migrate between Arctic and Southern Pacific ocean waters. The western or Korean population migrates between Siberia and South Korea. This population is probably almost extinct.

The eastern or Californian population migrates between the Bering Sea and the southern coast of California. It has recovered well from a devastating century of whaling, which ended in the 1940s. Today the population numbers are estimated to be more than 15,000.

CALIFORNIAN MIGRATION

The Californian Grey whales make an annual migration of up to 20,000km. They keep quite close to the North American coast in waters less than 100m deep.

In the summer the whales feed in the nutrient-rich waters of the Bering Sea. They put on weight fast, building up a thick blubber layer beneath the skin. They need this blubber as an energy store, because when they migrate they eat very little.

They start moving south in the autumn, reaching southern California by December. There they mate. By March they are heading north again for their summer feeding grounds.

The pattern is repeated each year. In December, in the seas around California, the females that became pregnant the previous year give birth.

▲With most of its gigantic body submerged, a Grey whale blows, expelling stale air from its lungs. It may do this up to five times after surfacing.

NURSING MOTHERS

The whale young, or calf, measures nearly 5m at birth. It has difficulty in breathing and swimming at first, and often the mother has to support it on the surface with her back or tail fins. The mother's teats are hidden, but they spurt milk into the calf's mouth when it nuzzles the right spot.

The calves stay close to their mothers on the long migration north in the spring. By the time they reach the northern feeding grounds they have become skilful swimmers and have built up a thick insulating layer of blubber.

RORQUALS

The 60-tonne bulk of a Humpback whale surges upwards through the water, driven by thrusts of its powerful tail. It breaks the surface and arches into the air, then falls back with a loud smack that makes the sea boil. No other whale performs this action, called breaching, so acrobatically.

RORQUALS
Balaenopteridae (*6 species*)

■ Diet: plankton, krill, fish.

◎ Breeding: 1 offspring after pregnancy of 10-12 months.

Size: smallest (Minke whale): head-body 11m, weight 10 tonnes; largest (Blue whale): head-body 27m, weight 150 tonnes.

Colour: black or blue-grey, often white underneath.

Lifespan: 45 years (Minke whale) to 95 years (Humpback whale).

Species mentioned in text:
Blue whale (*Balaenoptera musculus*)
Fin whale (*B. physalus*)
Humpback whale (*Megaptera novaeangliae*)
Minke whale (*Balaenoptera acutorostrata*)
Sei whale (*B. borealis*)

○ ◪ ☠
≋ Habitat: all main oceans.

1

2

▼**Species of rorqual** Five of the six rorquals. Humpback whale "breaching" **(1)**. Smallest of the rorquals, the Minke whale **(2)**. Bryde's whale (*Balaenoptera edeni*) **(3)**. Blue whale **(4)** – the slightly smaller Pygmy blue whale (*B. musculus brevicauda*) is found in southern waters. Fin whale **(5)**, which may have most baleen plates and throat-grooves.

▲The head of a Blue whale breaks the surface. It is sucking in air through the blowholes, ready for its next dive into the deeps.

The family of whales known as the rorquals includes the largest animal that has ever lived on this planet, the Blue whale. When fully grown, the Blue whale weighs more than 30 African bull elephants and is as long as eight cars placed bumper to bumper. The Fin whale grows almost as long, although it is slimmer and only about half the weight. Then in order of bulk come the Sei, Humpback, Bryde's and Minke whales.

The great stocks of these whales that once lived in the oceans have been devastated by whaling. Thousands were killed each year. Now they are protected, but they are still vulnerable to other hazards, such as pollution.

FILTER-FEEDERS
Like all whales, the rorquals are mammals. They are filter-feeders,

straining their food from the water using comb-like plates of baleen (whalebone) in their upper jaws. First they take a mouthful of water containing food and then force the water out through the baleen. The food gets trapped by bristles on the plates and is then swallowed.

All the rorquals have folds or grooves in the throat extending back along the belly. They allow the whales to increase enormously the volume of their mouths when gulping water to feed.

The favourite food of the rorquals is krill, a shrimp-like creature a few centimetres long. An adult Blue whale can eat as much as 2½ tonnes of krill every day.

Smaller plankton called copepods and fish such as herring, mackerel and cod are also part of the rorquals' diet. The water-thumping behaviour of breaching may be one way in which whales help scare and concentrate the fish before they feed.

GRACE AND PACE

Despite their huge bulk, the rorquals are graceful swimmers. Their bodies are beautifully streamlined, and they propel themselves by up and down movements of their large tail fins. The Sei whale is probably the fastest swimmer, able to reach speeds of 35kph for short periods.

Rorquals use the flippers on the sides of the body to steer. The flippers of the Humpback are especially large and have a jagged leading edge. All the whales have a small dorsal (back) fin to the rear of the body.

Other body features include a ridge between the snout and the blowholes (the whale's nostrils). The whale breathes out of the blowholes after surfacing, sending a spout of spray into the air.

BREEDING CYCLE

Rorquals are found in all major oceans of the world, the Atlantic, Pacific and Indian, in both Northern and Southern hemispheres. Most species spend the summer feeding in polar waters, where plankton and fish abound. They migrate south from the Northern hemisphere or north from the Southern hemisphere to winter in warmer waters. There they mate.

Males and pregnant females return to their feeding grounds for the summer, and the cycle begins again. When next they return to the warm water breeding grounds, the pregnant females give birth to their calves (young). They usually suckle their calves for 6 or 7 months, by which time they are back feeding again.

HAUNTING MELODY

As well as being a skilful acrobat, the Humpback whale is a fine singer. Most whales communicate with each other by sound – but while the others squeak and grunt, the Humpback sings a haunting melody.

The Humpback's song is made up of six basic themes, repeated over and over again. Each song can last for up to 35 minutes and may form part of a much longer recital. The variety of notes the animal uses have been described as resembling snores, whos, yups, chirps, ees and oos.

The whales' songs are studied using hydrophones (underwater microphones). Scientists have found that all the whales within a certain region of ocean sing much the same song. But the song changes according to the region and the season. The animals sing mainly when in shallow coastal waters and can keep in touch with one another over distances of more than 185km.

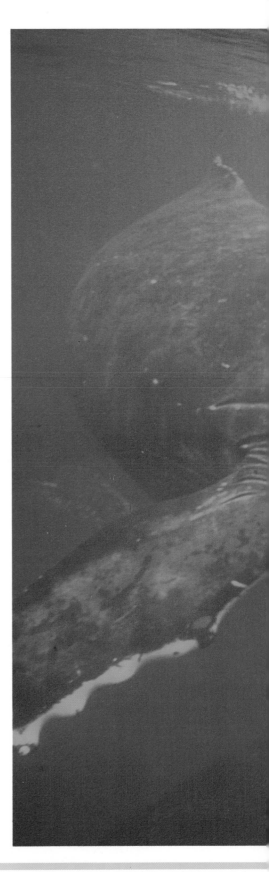

► Underwater photographs of rorquals, such as these Humpback whales, show that the body is sleek and pointed towards the snout and not baggy as previously thought from dead animals seen floating at the surface or pulled out of the water.

RIGHT WHALES

RIGHT WHALES
Balaenidae (*3 species*)

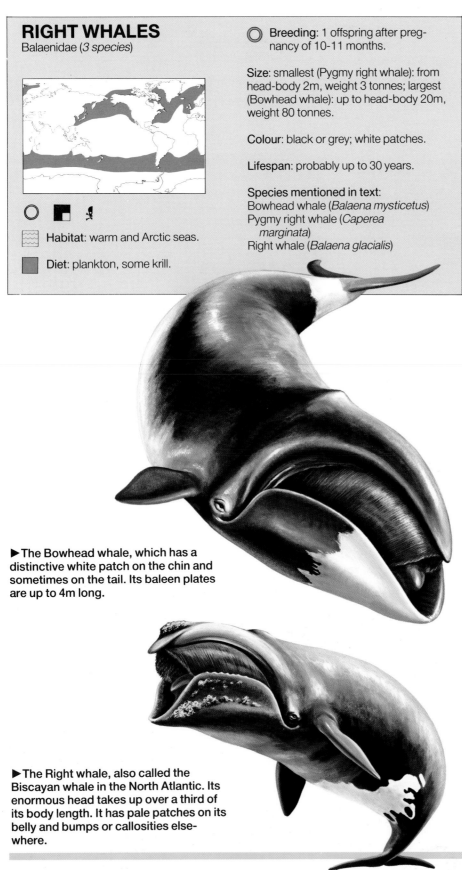

○ ■◻ ☠

▨ Habitat: warm and Arctic seas.

■ Diet: plankton, some krill.

○ Breeding: 1 offspring after pregnancy of 10-11 months.

Size: smallest (Pygmy right whale): from head-body 2m, weight 3 tonnes; largest (Bowhead whale): up to head-body 20m, weight 80 tonnes.

Colour: black or grey; white patches.

Lifespan: probably up to 30 years.

Species mentioned in text:
Bowhead whale (*Balaena mysticetus*)
Pygmy right whale (*Caperea marginata*)
Right whale (*Balaena glacialis*)

▶The Bowhead whale, which has a distinctive white patch on the chin and sometimes on the tail. Its baleen plates are up to 4m long.

▶The Right whale, also called the Biscayan whale in the North Atlantic. Its enormous head takes up over a third of its body length. It has pale patches on its belly and bumps or callosities elsewhere.

The Right whales are gathering in their breeding-grounds around the Bay of Fundy. Several can be seen travelling slowly on the surface. Over the still air come strange bellowing sounds like the lowing of cattle. The whales are calling to one another.

The Right whale was so called by the early whalers. It was the "right" whale to hunt because it yielded much oil and baleen (whalebone) and remained afloat when killed. And it was hunted, along with the Bowhead, almost to extinction. Despite protection, stocks of both whales are dangerously low, with a few thousand left.

The Right whale is much more vocal than the other two species of the right whale family, the Bowhead and Pygmy right whales. Both the Right whale and the Bowhead have an enormous mouth and long baleen plates. They use these to filter their food from the sea, like all the baleen whales. But they feed mainly on the surface, as does the Pygmy right whale.

▲A southern Right whale and her calf in the warm shallow waters off Argentina. On the beach are basking elephant seals. In this species of whale, mating often takes place in waters only 5 to 20m deep.

▲A Right whale "lob tails", bringing its tail crashing down on the surface, before it dives. No one knows why it does this – probably it is just for fun.

▼This Right whale is feeding at the surface in water rich in plankton. The food is strained through the long baleen plates on its upper jaw.

BUMPS AND BARNACLES
Both the Right and the Bowhead whales have black skin marked with white patches. But the Right whale can easily be recognised by the bumps or outgrowths on its skin (one of these, known as the bonnet, is always present on the top of the whale's head). The Bowhead has none, nor has the grey-skinned Pygmy right whale.

These outgrowths, called callosities, are covered in barnacles and lice. They are usually found on the snout, under the jaw, over the eye, along the bottom lip and around the blowholes. The pattern of callosities is unique to each animal and so helps scientists to recognise individuals from some distance away.

WHALE POPULATIONS
There are several groups or populations of Right whales in both the Northern and Southern hemispheres. They live in warm or cool temperate waters. One population migrates between the Carolinas (winter) and Newfoundland (summer) off the eastern, Atlantic coast of North America. Southern populations winter around South America, South Africa, Australia and New Zealand, spending the summer feeding near Antarctica.

Bowheads spend most of their time in Arctic waters. One of the biggest populations feeds in the Beaufort Sea in summer and migrates south to the Bering Sea for winter.

In common with most other whales the Right and Bowhead whales tend to follow a two-year breeding cycle that fits in with the north-south migration. Mating and calving usually take place in the warmer winter waters.

Not much is known about the breeding habits of the Pygmy right whale, which lives in the temperate seas of the Southern Ocean.

SEA COWS

A pair of nostrils break the surface of the murky water, and then their owner dives again. It is over a minute before the nostrils appear once more. Below the water the dugong is busy, digging up the roots of sea-grass and chewing them. Just out from the shore other dugongs are feeding on the sea-grass beds, but they take little notice of one another. But when a small motor boat chugs past, several raise their heads to peer at the intruder.

There are four living species of sea cow. The dugong is found in coastal shallows from the South-west Pacific to the coast of East Africa. The West Indian manatee lives in coastal waters, estuaries and rivers from Florida, through the Caribbean, to Brazil. The West African manatee lives in similar habitats down the coast of tropical West Africa, while the Amazonian manatee lives entirely in river water.

DIET OF SEA PLANTS

Sea cows live in tropical waters where sea-grasses (similar to the grasses that grow on land) grow in the shallows.

They do not eat seaweed. Much of the goodness of the sea-grasses is in their underground stems, and sea cows dig these up and eat them as well as the leaves. To deal with their tough plant

▼ **Species of sea cow** Steller's sea cow (*Hydrodamalis gigas*) is extinct **(1)**. 8m long and weighing 6 tonnes, it lived in the cold Northern Pacific. It was discovered by Europeans in 1741 and all were killed by 1768. The Amazonian manatee **(2)** feeds on floating vegetation. The West African manatee **(3)** has the strong bristles and mobile lips typical of sea cows. A West Indian manatee **(4)** carries some food in its flippers. The dugong **(5)** tail is forked, not round as in manatees.

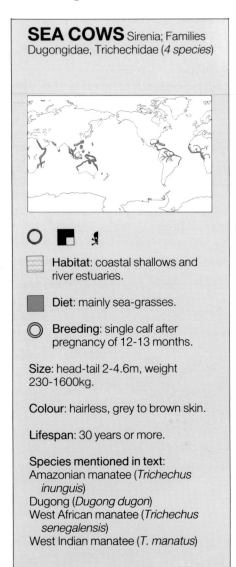

SEA COWS Sirenia; Families Dugongidae, Trichechidae (*4 species*)

○ ■ ☠

〰 Habitat: coastal shallows and river estuaries.

■ Diet: mainly sea-grasses.

◎ Breeding: single calf after pregnancy of 12-13 months.

Size: head-tail 2-4.6m, weight 230-1600kg.

Colour: hairless, grey to brown skin.

Lifespan: 30 years or more.

Species mentioned in text:
Amazonian manatee (*Trichechus inunguis*)
Dugong (*Dugong dugon*)
West African manatee (*Trichechus senegalensis*)
West Indian manatee (*T. manatus*)

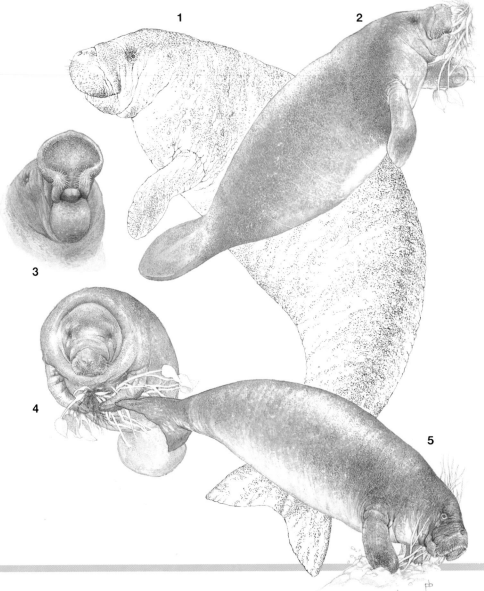

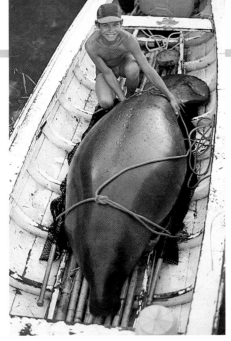

▲A manatee is captured for transport to another area where it will be used to control water-weed in a dammed lake.

▼Body contact such as "kissing" (1) takes place between manatees. The only constant social group seems to be mother and young (2). Manatees may rest on the bottom on their back (3). They use rubbing posts (4) for scent marking.

food, manatees have intestines more than 45m long.

Sea cows are streamlined for swimming, although they rarely swim fast. They do not have back legs while their forelimbs are flippers which help in steering, but are flexible enough to help gather food. The tail is horizontally flattened for swimming. The fat that sea cows store under their skin helps keep them warm, but they still avoid temperatures below 20°C. Sea cows' bodies work at only a third of the rate of most mammals.

Manatees have teeth which grow forward, wear away and are replaced from the back. This makes up for the toughness of their food. Dugong teeth are even odder. The dugong has a pair of short tusks, then a few peg-like teeth at the back of the mouth. The work of chewing is done by horny plates covering the palate and the front of the lower jaw.

The dugong rakes in food using its mobile top lip and bristles. The muscles contract in waves to extract food items and pass them back to the grinding jaws. The dugong digs most of its food from the floor of the shallows with its snout, earning it the alternative name of sea-pig.

The West Indian and African manatees also forage on the bottom. The Amazonian manatee usually feeds on plants which grow on the surface.

GENTLE HELPERS
Dugongs sometimes occur in herds of several hundred, and manatees in herds of a dozen. Yet these animals seem to be basically solitary, having no herd organization. They breed slowly – a female dugong may live 50 years but will produce only six young. The baby is suckled for nearly 2 years. It is 8 years old before it breeds.

Sea cows are gentle creatures. For years they have been hunted for their meat, oil and hide. Now they are in demand to help clear waterways and lakes of vegetation.

HYRAXES

On top of a rocky outcrop in Tanzania's Serengeti National Park, about 30 hyraxes huddle together in the early morning Sun. As they warm up, the youngsters begin to play, and some of the adults wander off to feed. Suddenly the peace is broken by a shrill whistle of alarm from a large male acting as look-out. The hyraxes dive for cover as an eagle plunges out of the Sun.

Anyone seeing a hyrax for the first time would probably think it was a relative of the guinea pigs or the hamsters. But far from being related to the rodents, the hyrax is a distant relative of the biggest land animal on Earth – the elephant! The connection is a very distant one, but both elephants and hyraxes are descendants of the same group of prehistoric hoofed animals.

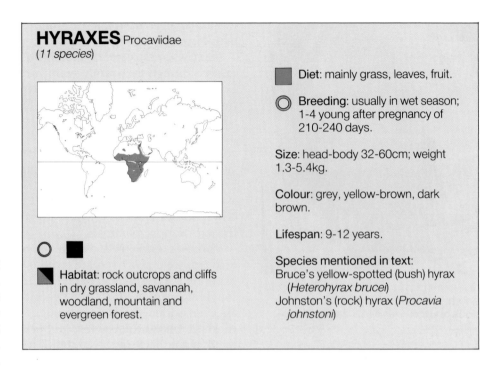

HYRAXES Procaviidae
(11 species)

■ **Diet:** mainly grass, leaves, fruit.

◯ **Breeding:** usually in wet season; 1-4 young after pregnancy of 210-240 days.

Size: head-body 32-60cm; weight 1.3-5.4kg.

Colour: grey, yellow-brown, dark brown.

Lifespan: 9-12 years.

Species mentioned in text:
Bruce's yellow-spotted (bush) hyrax (*Heterohyrax brucei*)
Johnston's (rock) hyrax (*Procavia johnstoni*)

◯ ■
◨ **Habitat:** rock outcrops and cliffs in dry grassland, savannah, woodland, mountain and evergreen forest.

▼Hyraxes, like this Johnston's hyrax of north-east Africa and the south-east Arabian Peninsula, will put up a ferocious fight if attacked or cornered.

▶Bush hyraxes, such as Bruce's yellow-spotted hyrax, sometimes inhabit hollow trees, but usually they live in holes in rock outcrops.

KINGS OF THE KOPJES

Hyraxes are divided into three groups. Most widespread are the rock hyraxes or dassies of the savannah woodlands, plains and highlands. Like the bush hyraxes of East Africa, they live on small rocky outcrops locally called kopjes, and on cliffs. Tree hyraxes inhabit woodland and rain forests across central Africa, but they too are found among the barren rocks of the Ruwenzori mountains.

All the hyraxes are plant-eaters. Rock hyraxes eat mainly coarse grass while the others eat softer leaves, fruit and occasionally birds' eggs and insects. Strangely, a hyrax's teeth are not well suited to this diet. The tusk-like incisors are hardly used so the animal has to turn its head to one side and use its sharp cheek teeth.

Most of the hyraxes live in dry habitats so their bodies are designed to conserve water. Their urine is very concentrated, and contains large amounts of waste chemicals, including calcium carbonate. As the animals always use the same toilet areas (latrines), the rocks there soon become coated with white limestone crystals.

LIVING TOGETHER

Hyraxes are very sociable animals. They live in groups of up to 50, and a group will often contain roughly equal numbers of two different species.

Living in groups has many advantages. Hyraxes are not very good at controlling their body temperature, so when they leave their sleeping holes in the morning they huddle together for warmth. There is safety in numbers too. Whenever the animals are feeding, at least one senior adult is always on guard duty.

Even though two species may live together, each will breed only with its own kind. Females become pregnant once a year, and young are usually born in the rainy seasons, when food is in plentiful supply.

The 11 present-day species of hyrax are found throughout Africa south of the Sahara, and one group, the rock hyraxes, also live in the Middle East.

RUBBER-SOLED SPRINTERS

Despite their chunky bodies and short legs, hyraxes are outstanding climbers and jumpers. The undersides of their feet have thick rubbery pads with large numbers of sweat glands, and as the animals run the sweat makes the pads sticky. This allows the hyraxes to dash up and down steep rocks and tree trunks with astonishing agility. This speed is important to the hyraxes' survival, for these small mammals are favourite prey for eagles, owls, leopards, jackals, hyenas and many kinds of snake.

ELEPHANTS

In the blazing red of an African sunset, a herd of elephants makes its way down to the river bank. In the middle of the herd, close to their mothers, are two young babies. Suddenly the leader stops. She puts up her trunk and fans out her ears. She senses danger. The elephants halt and bunch up. From some thorn bushes two lionesses appear. The leading elephant gives a squeal of rage, tucks up her trunk and charges. The lions scatter. No other animal stays in the path of a charging elephant.

ELEPHANTS Elephantidae
(2 species)

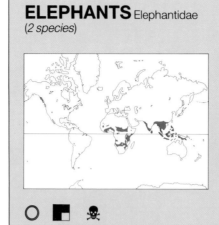

○ ◧ ☠

◢ Habitat: forest and savannah grassland.

■ Diet: grasses, shrubs and trees, including twigs, leaves and bark.

○ Breeding: usually during the annual wet season. 1 young after pregnancy of 22 months.

Size: to 3.3m in height, 6,000kg in weight. Females shorter, to 4,000kg.

Colour: grey-black, sometimes with pinkish patches. Often appears red-brown from dust thrown over body.

Lifespan: 60 years.

Species mentioned in text:
African elephant (*Loxodonta africana*)
Asian elephant (*Elephas maximus*)

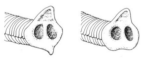

▲The Asian elephant (bottom) is smaller than the African and has smaller ears. It has a single lip, not two, at the trunk tip.

►Elephants have a good sense of smell. Trunks are held high to catch scents.

120

The African elephant is the biggest living land animal. The slightly smaller Asian species is rare now as a wild animal, and only about 50,000 are left.

GIANTS OF THE LAND

The biggest African elephant ever measured stood 4m tall, about as high as a bungalow. It was a male (bull) elephant. These often reach 3.2m tall, and nearly 6 tonnes in weight. Females (cows) are shorter, and weigh up to 4 tonnes. The biggest African elephants are those from savannah country. Those from forests near the equator are usually smaller, and have rounder ears.

Since elephants are so big, they have problems keeping cool. Their ears give a large surface from which heat can be lost. The elephants also use them as fans.

GIANT APPETITES

Elephants have an appetite to go with their size. An adult needs about 150kg of plant food a day. This is equal to about six small bales of hay. But much of the food is of poor quality. Bacteria in the gut help the elephant break down its food. Even so, nearly half passes through the elephant without being digested. Elephants have to spend about 16 hours out of every 24 feeding. Water too is drunk in large amounts. An elephant needs about 80 litres a day (equal to 140 pint bottles of milk).

TRUNK CALLS

An elephant gathers all its food and water with its trunk. This is a combined nose and upper lip. The trunk is full of muscles which can move it in all directions with precision or strength. It can be used to pick a single leaf or berry, using the "lips" at the tip. Or instead, it may be used to rip a branch from a tree before lifting it to the mouth. Water is always sucked into the trunk, then squirted into the mouth and swallowed. Another use for the trunk is as a snorkel when bathing.

▲Where their numbers are high, elephants can cause enormous changes to an area by uprooting trees to feed on their tops.

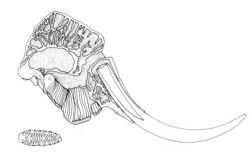

▲In the elephant's huge skull 24 chewing teeth grow in sequence. Of these only four are used at a time. When worn, they are lost and replaced from behind.

The trunk is also important in making sounds, and helping elephants to "keep in touch". Elephants greet one another by putting the trunk tip to the other's mouth. Mothers reassure their babies (calves) by touching and guiding them with the trunk. Sniffing and touching with the trunk tells an elephant much about its surroundings.

LIVING TOGETHER

Adult bull elephants live alone, or sometimes in small groups. They join the females only for mating. Cow elephants live in herds accompanied by their calves. Bulls leave the herd as they become adult, but cows stay with their mother. The herd is usually led by the oldest and largest cow, the matriarch. She, by example, shows when and where to move. She also decides how to react to threats. She

may charge an enemy, or lead the herd away. An elephant's lifespan is nearly as long as a human's. The leader has had time to learn many useful things. By following her behaviour, other cows in the herd can gain experience for the time when they may have to lead a herd. The matriarch is often too old to produce young.

BIG BABIES

The elephant has the longest pregnancy of all mammals. At birth, the newborn baby weighs 120kg – more than most adult humans. It sucks milk from its mother using its mouth, not its trunk. In the first months the trunk is almost useless. The calf takes milk until about 2 years old, but eats plants after only a few months.

Elephants grow fast until they are about 15 years old. After this growth

◀In Asia people have used elephants for thousands of years. A few are still used for work in some timber forests. They can move logs over a tonne in weight and can work where tractors cannot.

The elephant's most important teeth are the huge grinding cheek teeth. Without these it cannot eat properly. An old elephant which has worn down its last teeth will starve.

ELEPHANTS AND PEOPLE

Although elephants are so big, people can tame and train them. Working elephants are usually females, as these are better tempered than males. People have used Asian elephants much more than African ones for working, but the African general Hannibal crossed the Alps with 57 African war elephants on his way to attack Rome in 218 BC. Tame elephants, often painted or with bright costumes, take part in some Asian festivals. In some places light-coloured ("white") elephants are especially respected.

HEADING FOR EXTINCTION?

Hunting for ivory to make ornaments is perhaps the greatest danger facing elephants. Each year, about 100,000 African elephants are killed, most of them illegally, for their tusks. Also, as human numbers increase, farms are built where elephants used to roam freely. When crammed together, elephants destroy habitats. Occasionally they must be culled. In Africa there may still be a million elephants, but their numbers are falling fast.

may slow down, but elephants, unlike many mammals, go on growing throughout life. Their tusks too continually grow.

WORLD'S BIGGEST TEETH

The elephant's tusks are simply enormous front (incisor) teeth. The tough material of which they are made is known as ivory. The longest tusk on record was 3.5m long. The heaviest pair known weighed a total of 211kg. Most are much smaller, but, even so, a big bull elephant carries a great weight in tusks. Cows have smaller, more slender, tusks. In Asian elephants the tusks of cows are so small they hardly stick out beyond the lips. The tusks are occasionally used in feeding, or may be used to threaten or fight a rival. But most of the time they are used very little.

▲Bull elephants sometimes fight one another for the chance of mating with a cow who is on heat.

Fighting consists of charges and shoving matches. Sometimes the trunk and tusks are used in wrestling.

Usually the smaller elephant gives way once it has tested its strength. Only rarely is one of the animals hurt.

HORSES AND ASSES

A herd of wild horses moves slowly forwards, heads down, cropping grass. The only adult male lifts his head, alerted by the arrival of a male horse from another herd. He walks to challenge it. The stranger hesitates. The herd master drops his head and charges, baring his teeth as if to bite. The stranger turns and flees. The herd goes back to grazing.

HORSES AND ASSES
Equidae (*4 species*)

○　■　☠

● Habitat: grassland, open plain and desert.

■ Diet: mainly grasses, some bark, leaves and fruits.

○ Breeding: 1 or 2 foals after pregnancy of 11½ months, at the season when plant growth is best. Females mate soon after giving birth.

Size: head-body 2-2.1m plus 49cm tail; weight 275-350kg.

Colour: yellowish-brown to grey, lighter below. Tail and mane darker, often a dark back stripe.

Lifespan: 25 years.

Species mentioned in text:
African ass *(Equus africanus)*
Asiatic ass *(E. hemionus)*
Domestic horse *(E. caballus)*
Przewalski's horse *(E. przewalskii)*

There are three species of wild horses and asses plus the Domestic horse, of which there are many breeds. Wild horses live mostly on open plains in dry regions. Przewalski's horse is native to Mongolia. It is probably extinct in the wild. None have been seen there since 1968. Another form of the same species, the Tarpan, used to live on the European steppes. These wild horses were the ancestors of our domestic horses.

The Asiatic ass is a strongly built animal with broad hoofs that lives in deserts. There are four slightly different races, all existing in small numbers. The African wild ass roams rocky deserts in North Africa. It is the smallest of the horse family, and is the ancestor of the domestic donkey.

Asses withstand water loss well, and can journey far to find sparse supplies of food and water. But even in deserts they are not always safe from humans, and numbers are declining.

LIVING IN THE OPEN
Horses and asses are built for eating grass and running fast to escape danger. They gather grass with their lips and the top and bottom front teeth (incisors). Their chewing teeth and gut can cope with tough grasses.

Horses have long legs, each with a single hoof, or toe-nail. The legs are light and easy to swing when running. A wild horse can run at speeds of 50kph, and has plenty of stamina.

Horses have keen eyes. These are set far back on the head, and they can see danger from all directions. Their hearing is excellent, and the sense of smell is good. Voice plays a part in social behaviour, and so does scent. Horses indicate moods to one another by changing ear, mouth and tail positions.

CHANGED BY HUMANS
Over the years people have bred wild horses for particular jobs. There are now breeds as different as carthorses, taller than a man, and Shetland ponies, only waist-high.

Domestic horses have a mane that falls sideways, unlike that of any wild species. The big herds of "wild" horses seen in America and Australia are descended from tame ones allowed to run loose.

▶Wild species of the horse family
A Przewalski's horse **(1)** (male) charges a rival. An African ass **(2)** lashes out with her feet. An Asiatic ass marks territory with a dung-heap **(3)** and curls its lip as it sniffs a female **(4)**.

▼No modern species of horse lived in America until introduced by Europeans in the 16th century. Then, allowed to go wild, they became the mustangs used by Plains Indians and cowboys.

ZEBRAS

A long column of zebras crosses the dry plain, each animal following the ones in front. They are in search of water. Suddenly a leopard drops to the ground from the branch of a tree, just missing a foal that is lagging behind its mother. There is a moment of panic. Zebras dash in circles, creating a confusing mass of black and white. The foal escapes. As the disappointed leopard stalks off, calm returns. The zebras plod on towards the next river.

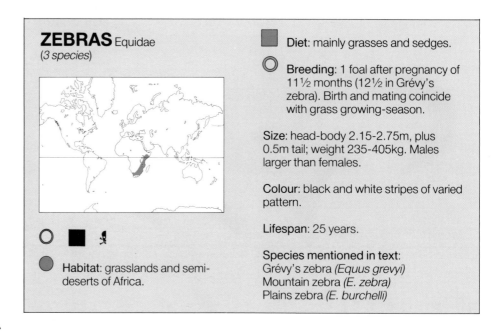

ZEBRAS Equidae
(3 species)

○ ■ ☠

● Habitat: grasslands and semi-deserts of Africa.

■ Diet: mainly grasses and sedges.

○ Breeding: 1 foal after pregnancy of 11½ months (12½ in Grévy's zebra). Birth and mating coincide with grass growing-season.

Size: head-body 2.15-2.75m, plus 0.5m tail; weight 235-405kg. Males larger than females.

Colour: black and white stripes of varied pattern.

Lifespan: 25 years.

Species mentioned in text:
Grévy's zebra *(Equus grevyi)*
Mountain zebra *(E. zebra)*
Plains zebra *(E. burchelli)*

A zebra is a striped horse. There are three species of zebra. Apart from stripes, and the fact that they all live in Africa, the species have little in common, and are only related genetically.

WHY BE STRIPED?
There are various ideas about why it is useful to a zebra to have stripes. One theory is that the stripes are mainly for use among zebras, as a bright signal that allows them to follow one another's movements. Zebras certainly seem to be attracted by stripes. Perhaps at times there are other uses for stripes, such as camouflage.

MIGRATING MULTITUDES
The most numerous of the zebras is the Plains zebra, found from South to East Africa. In many areas its broad black stripes and rather dumpy body are a familiar sight. The Plains zebras of some areas, such as the Serengeti and Botswana, make long migrations to make use of seasonal growth of grass. At this time many thousands of zebras may move together, but for most of the year the typical herd is a

▶A herd of Plains zebras drinks at a waterhole in Etosha National Park in Namibia.

◀Each zebra has a unique pattern of stripes. This may help them recognize one another. This zebra is unusually marked.

male (stallion) and his group of females (mares) and their young (foals).

THREATENED ZEBRAS

The Mountain zebra is found in mountain grasslands of south-west Africa. It has narrower stripes than the Plains zebra and a fold of skin, the dewlap, under the throat. It has a "grid-iron" arrangement of stripes over the rump. It lives in small herds. Populations are small. They are protected in national parks, but this species is listed as vulnerable.

Grévy's zebra lives in northern East Africa. It is the largest zebra, and has the narrowest stripes. It has a tall mane and big rounded ears. It lives in small herds in thorn scrub country. Once fairly common, it has been hunted for its beautiful coat in recent years. It is now endangered.

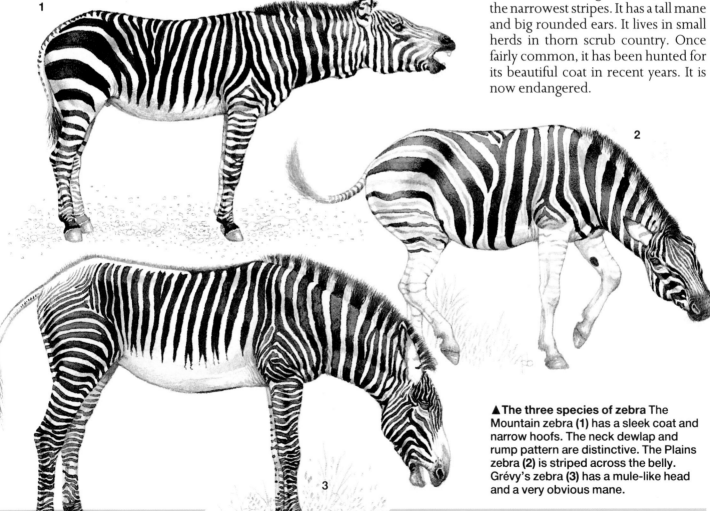

▲The three species of zebra The Mountain zebra (1) has a sleek coat and narrow hoofs. The neck dewlap and rump pattern are distinctive. The Plains zebra (2) is striped across the belly. Grévy's zebra (3) has a mule-like head and a very obvious mane.

TAPIRS

A nose appears out of the jungle river and cautiously sniffs the air. Satisfied that the scent which alarmed it has gone, the nose's owner hauls itself out of the water and on to the bank, to resume the night's feeding. Sniffing and feeling with its flexible nose, the tapir chooses the choicest morsels from the bushes as it passes. It forces its bulky body between the bushes, then walks along the same well-worn track that it took to the water.

▲ Tapirs like water, and will also wallow in mud.

TAPIRS Tapiridae (*4 species*)

● ■ ☠

 Habitat: forest and woodland, usually near water.

Diet: leaves, buds, twigs, fruits, and grasses.

Breeding: 1 young after pregnancy of 390-400 days.

Size: head-body 1.8-2.5m; shoulder height 0.75-1.2m; weight 225-300kg.

Colour: dark to reddish-brown in American species, black and white in Malayan. Young of all species with longitudinal stripes.

Lifespan: 30 years.

Species mentioned in text:
Malayan tapir (*Tapirus indicus*)
Mountain tapir (*T. pinchaque*)

Tapirs live in two quite separate parts of the world. One species, the Malayan tapir, lives in South-east Asia. The other three live in Central and South America. Most tapirs inhabit lowland areas. The Mountain tapir inhabits mountain forests, and may wander above the tree-line.

SEARCHING SNOUT
Tapirs have a compact shape, ideal for pushing through dense jungle under-growth. The snout has a short, fleshy trunk. This is a combined nose and upper lip, and has nostrils at the tip. Tapirs use their trunk as a sensitive "finger" to pull leaves and shoots to the mouth. They eat many kinds of plant food, but prefer to browse on green shoots in forest clearings and along river banks.

3

Tapir tracks are often the only sign that the animals are around. They show three hoofed toes, although there is a small fourth toe on the front feet. Like rhinos and horses, tapirs take the weight down the middle toe of the feet. The side toes are smaller.

GUIDED BY SMELL

Tapirs are most active at night. They have large ears, and their hearing is good, but not as acute as the sense of smell. Their eyes are small and provide only reasonable vision. Tapirs walk with their nose to the ground. This helps them to sniff out where they are, and to detect the scent of other tapirs or predators. They follow familiar routes, and mark these with their urine.

Apart from mothers with young, tapirs usually live alone. They may range widely. They are good swimmers, and will take to water and submerge to avoid danger. Disturbed away from water, tapirs crash off into the bush, or defend themselves by biting. Mating starts with a noisy courtship. The pair of tapirs circles at speed and both animals squeal. They nip and prod each other. At the end of pregnancy, the female finds a secluded lair in which to give birth. Tapirs are fully adult at about 3 years old.

UNCERTAIN FUTURE

Tapirs are hunted for food, sport and for their thick skins, which give good leather. But the biggest threat to them is the loss of their habitat. Soon they may only survive in areas specially set aside for wildlife.

◀The species of tapir The Mountain tapir (1) has a woolly coat. The Brazilian tapir (*Tapirus terrestris*) (2) and Baird's tapir (*T. bairdi*) (3) have bristly manes. The black and white Malayan tapir (4) is hard to see at night. Baby tapirs lose their stripes by six months old.

RHINOCEROSES

An African Black rhinoceros wallows in a muddy pool, her tiny calf beside her. Suddenly sounds of movement come from a thicket not far away. The mother rhino stands up and charges towards the thicket. An animal scurries away. She stops, turns, and trots back to the calf.

RHINOCEROSES
Rhinocerotidae (*5 species*)

○ ■ ⚰

● Habitat: grassland, swamp and forest.

■ Diet: grass, leaves and shoot ends of shrubs.

◡ Breeding: 1 calf after pregnancy of 8-16 months.

Size: head-body 2.5-4.0m; weight 800-2,300kg.

Colour: greyish skin, hairless except in Sumatran rhino, which has sparse long reddish hair.

Lifespan: 45 years.

Species mentioned in text:
Black rhinoceros (*Diceros bicornis*)
Indian rhinoceros (*Rhinoceros unicornis*)
Javan rhinoceros (*R. sondaicus*)
Sumatran rhinoceros (*Dicerorhinus sumatrensis*)
White rhinoceros (*Ceratotherium simum*)

There are five species of rhinoceros. The Black rhino and the White rhino both live in Africa. They differ little in colour, and both have two horns, but they can be told apart by the shape of their faces. The Black rhino is a browsing animal, feeding on leaves from bushes. It has a long pointed upper lip which helps it pull food into its mouth. The White rhino is a grazer, and has a wide muzzle. It crops many blades of grass at once.

The other three species of rhino live in Asia. The Indian rhino has an armour-plated look, with big folds of skin above the legs. This, and the African White rhino, are the two biggest species. Males grow to 1.85m tall and 2.3 tonnes in weight, and females to 1.7m and 1.7 tonnes. The Javan rhino is smaller and has less obvious body folds. The Indian and the Javan rhino have only one horn.

The smallest rhino is the Sumatran, which has two horns, and has a thin coat of reddish hair. Javan and Sumatran rhinos browse from bushes and saplings. Indian rhinos pull in shrubs and tall grass with the upper lip, but can fold the tip away to graze short grass.

HORNS AND HAIR
Rhino horns are unusual in that they lie along the middle of the snout and, unlike the horns of sheep, cattle and antelope, they do not have a bony centre. They are not firmly attached to the skull. Rhino horns grow from the skin, and are made of the same chemical as hair and claws. They are hard and solid, but are made up of many fibres. African rhinos sometimes have front horns 1.6m in length.

Except in the Sumatran rhino, hair is only visible as eyelashes, ear fringes and tail tassels. These animals do not need fur to keep warm.

SENSES
Rhinos rely mostly on their sense of smell to explore their surroundings.

▲Rhino courtship and mating may take several hours. Courtship is rough, with long chases and "fights" – sparring with the horns – between male and female.

They have rather poor vision. They cannot pick out a person standing still more than 30m away. Their hearing is good, and they turn their tubular ear flaps towards sounds in which they are interested. Rhinos can make many sounds, from roars and squeals to bleats which sound too gentle for such massive animals.

Partly because of their poor vision, perhaps, some species are apt to make sudden charges at intruders. The Black rhino has a reputation for aggression, and the Indian rhino too may make apparently unprovoked attacks. Most rhino charges are not carried through. African rhinos attack with their horns, but the Asian species may bite a supposed enemy. These are the same methods that male rhinos use when fighting each other.

SOLITARY LIFE-STYLE
Most rhinos live alone. A calf may stay with its mother for 2 or 3 years. Sometimes several rhinos are found together around a good feeding site. But most rhinos prefer to be by themselves.

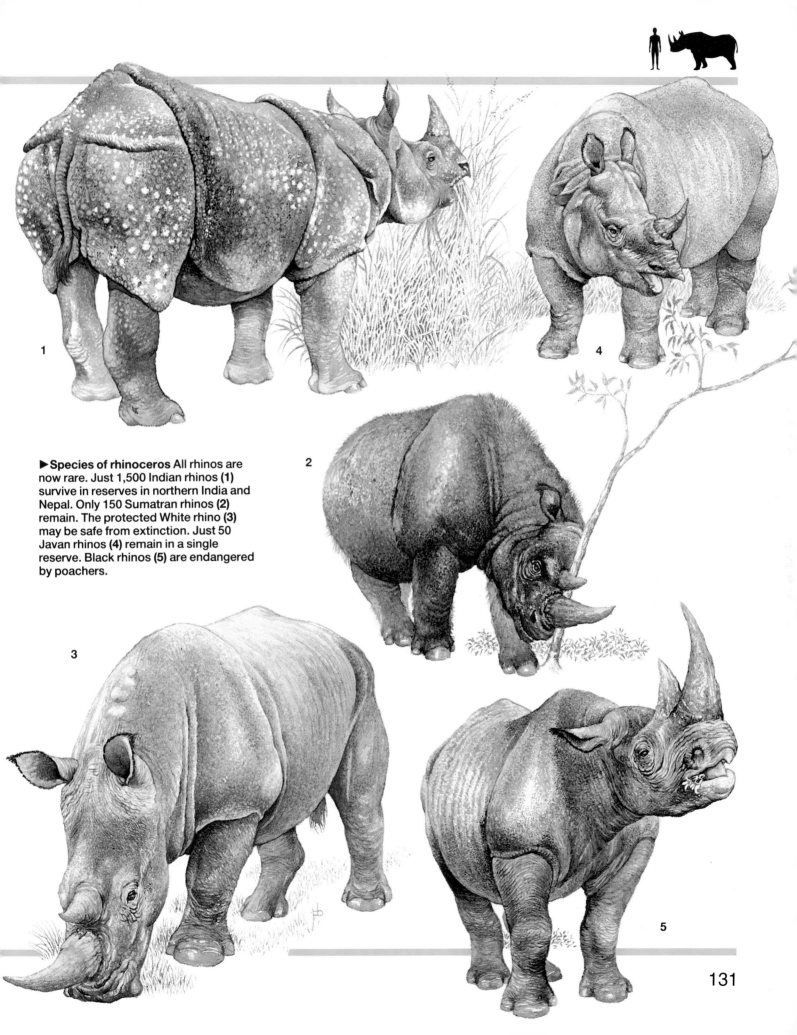

▶**Species of rhinoceros** All rhinos are now rare. Just 1,500 Indian rhinos **(1)** survive in reserves in northern India and Nepal. Only 150 Sumatran rhinos **(2)** remain. The protected White rhino **(3)** may be safe from extinction. Just 50 Javan rhinos **(4)** remain in a single reserve. Black rhinos **(5)** are endangered by poachers.

The exception is the White rhino, which may form small herds of six or seven animals. Even so, adult males are usually solitary.

Adult males often claim an area for themselves, keeping out other males. These may be repelled by ritual fighting, such as sparring with horns, or wiping the horns on the ground. Sometimes a real battle begins, and the animals wound one another. Usually, the rituals are enough to keep the males spread apart. They also mark the edges of their territories with special piles of dung and urine.

LIFE HISTORY
Rhinos have long lives. They may be able to breed at 5 years old, but females bear a calf only every 2 or 3 years. Males may not be able to defend an area and breed until they are about 10 years old. Baby rhinos are small compared to their parents, weighing only about 40kg in the case of the Indian rhino, but they are still as heavy as most 12-year-old children. Rhino mothers usually find a quiet spot in which to give birth. They may leave tiny babies hidden while they feed elsewhere, but after a few days most baby rhinos move with their mother. Baby Indian and White rhinos tend to run in front of the mother, baby Black rhinos usually run behind.

SURVIVAL IN QUESTION
Some 40 million year ago, rhinos of various kinds were abundant in most warm regions of the world. Now these animals are in danger of extinction. They are hunted for their horn, which is believed to have medicinal properties. It is also used to make handles for daggers which are status symbols in parts of Arabia.

◄African White rhinos are usually peaceable and rather timid, in spite of their size. These grass-eaters are more often found in groups than other rhinos.

WILD PIGS

It is night in an African village. Once the people are asleep a family of bushpigs comes out of the forest into the villagers' small fields. Busily, they dig with their noses. They uproot and eat plants, and feed on small animals they disturb. By morning the pigs are gone, but patches in the fields look as if they had just been ploughed.

Three species of wild pig live in Africa. Four more live on islands in Southeast Asia. The smallest wild pig, the rare Pygmy hog, lives only in the tall grass of the Himalayan foothills. The most widespread wild pig is the Wild boar, found from Europe to eastern Asia. This is the species from which domestic pigs have been bred.

KNOWLEDGEABLE NOSES
All pigs have a large head and short neck. Their snout is very long, with a nose supported by a special movable bone. The end of the nose is round and flat like a disc. For pigs, the nose is a very important organ. It provides the

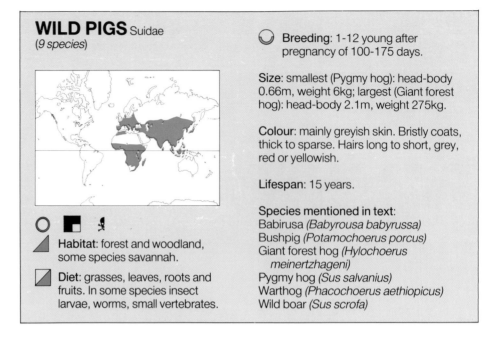

WILD PIGS Suidae
(*9 species*)

○ ■ ☠

△ **Habitat**: forest and woodland, some species savannah.

◹ **Diet**: grasses, leaves, roots and fruits. In some species insect larvae, worms, small vertebrates.

○ **Breeding**: 1-12 young after pregnancy of 100-175 days.

Size: smallest (Pygmy hog): head-body 0.66m, weight 6kg; largest (Giant forest hog): head-body 2.1m, weight 275kg.

Colour: mainly greyish skin. Bristly coats, thick to sparse. Hairs long to short, grey, red or yellowish.

Lifespan: 15 years.

Species mentioned in text:
Babirusa (*Babyrousa babyrussa*)
Bushpig (*Potamochoerus porcus*)
Giant forest hog (*Hylochoerus meinertzhageni*)
Pygmy hog (*Sus salvanius*)
Warthog (*Phacochoerus aethiopicus*)
Wild boar (*Sus scrofa*)

animals with a keen sense of smell, and a good sense of touch at the snout tip. The nose is also used to dig in earth in search of food. A large part of a pig's brain is devoted to the movement and sensitivity of its nose.

Pigs have a coat of coarse bristles and a tasselled tail which they use to swat flies and to signal moods to one

another. They have four toes on each foot. The outside two toes are small and do not usually touch the ground. Some wild pigs feed almost entirely on plants, but other members of the family eat small animals too.

CURVING CANINES
The tusks of wild pigs are big canine teeth. Both the lower and the upper tusks curve upwards and outwards. The tusks can be deadly weapons, and Wild boar especially will fight back hard if threatened. They will fight off

▼Species of wild pig fight in ways that reflect the shape and form of their weapons and armour. The Giant forest hog (1) fights head-on. Warthogs (2) and bushpigs (3) have warts to protect the face. Wild boar (4) slash at opponents' shoulders, where they have tough skin and hair.

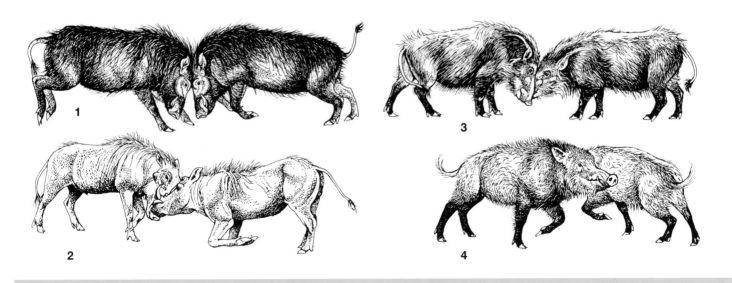

▲Although a Giant forest hog's upper tusks are more impressive, it is the smaller lower tusks that are the animal's main weapons.

▲A family of warthogs drinks at a pool. These African pigs often drink and feed on grass shoots and roots resting on their front "knees".

▼The Wild boar is one of the largest pigs. The shoulders are padded for protection in fights. In front of each eye is a slit containing a scent gland.

leopards or tigers. Warthogs also have big tusks, but they fight only as a last resort. Warthogs run from trouble with their tail held high like a flag. They will also take cover in burrows dug by other animals such as aardvarks.

The biggest tusks of all belong to the babirusa of Sulawesi and nearby Indonesian islands. This wild pig has upper tusks which grow straight up through

the skin of the snout and then curve backwards. Sometimes they grow right over the snout to touch the forehead. The lower tusks are long too. They seem to be useless as weapons, although they may help males impress one another when competing for females. In all pigs males have bigger tusks than females.

Several kinds of pig have large warts on their face. These, and other toughened parts of the head, give some protection when they are fighting one another.

FAMILY GROUPS

Pigs go about in groups, called sounders, made up of a mother (sow) and her young (piglets). Young of most species have a striped coat. Sometimes females that are old enough to breed stay with their mother, so the group is bigger. Adult males (boars) often live alone, but groups are sometimes found. The strongest males in an area mate with the females. Courtship involves communication using sounds, such as squeaks and grunts, and scents. Some pigs have special scent-producing glands in front of the eyes, on the lips, or on the feet. They use them to mark their home areas.

HIPPOPOTAMUSES

In a deep pool in an African river the fish swim lazily. A small crocodile drifts by. Suddenly a huge animal springs across the bottom of the pool in a slow motion gallop, lightly touching the bottom with its toes. Then it floats to the surface, where just its eyes, nose and ears peek above water. It is a hippopotamus. On land the animal is heavy and cumbersome. Buoyed up by the water it is almost weightless and moves easily and gracefully.

HIPPOPOTAMUSES
Hippopotamidae (*2 species*)

● ■ ☠

Habitat: lakes, wallows and rivers during day, grassland at night. Pygmy hippo in swamp forest.

Diet: mostly land vegetation, especially short grasses.

○ Breeding: 1 young after pregnancy of 190-240 days.

Size: Pygmy hippopotamus: head-body 1.5m; weight 180kg. Hippopotamus: head-body 3.45m; weight 3.2 tonnes. Males larger than females.

Colour: blackish grey, lighter or pinkish below.

Lifespan: 45 years.

Species mentioned in text:
Hippopotamus (*Hippopotamus amphibius*)
Pygmy hippopotamus (*Choeropsis liberiensis*)

▶ The hippo's lower tusks are up to 50cm long. They are used in fights between rival males. Adult males are often scarred.

The most familiar hippo is the larger of the two species. It is found in slow-moving rivers and lakes. It lives over much of Africa south of the Sahara where water and grassland are close to one another. The second species is the Pygmy hippo found in the forests of West Africa. This is a much rarer animal. It is tiny compared to its grassland cousin, and much more difficult to observe. Few details are known of its habits.

The common hippo has eyes, ears and nose at the very top of the head, so it can hear, see and breathe in air while mostly submerged. The nostrils and ears can be closed when under water. In the Pygmy hippo the eyes are further to the side of the head.

DAY-TIME LAZY-BONES
The common hippo spends most of the day in water. It seems to prefer slow-moving rivers, but also lives in lakes, and sometimes in estuaries. This aquatic habit takes the weight off its feet, and also prevents water loss through the skin. Water escapes through hippo skin four times as fast as through a person's in dry air. Hippo skin is smooth, with few hairs. Glands in the skin secrete a pink fluid which protects the skin from sunburn. Beneath the skin is a layer of fat 5cm

▶ Hippos feed on land but often get rid of waste food (defecate) in water, so adding fertilizer to the water. Some kinds of fish stay close to hippos, either to graze on tiny plants that grow on the hippos skin, or to feed on the dung.

thick, which keeps the hippo warm in cool water.

Day is a lazy time for the hippo. It rests, swims a little, submerges for up to 5 minutes, and yawns repeatedly.

NIGHT-TIME GRAZERS
At night the hippo emerges from the water. This is when it does all its feeding. For 6 hours or so, the hippo crops grass with its huge lips. Where possible it feeds on patches of short grasses, or hippo lawns, close to

◄A baby Pygmy hippo weighs about 4kg at birth. Pygmy hippos are less aquatic than common hippos, and feed on roots, shoots and fruit found on the forest floor and in swamps.

water, but sometimes has to travel several kilometres to find food. Hippos sometimes make long overland journeys to new bodies of water.

The strongest male in an area mates with all the females in it. He keeps rivals away by displays of yawning to show the teeth, by charges, and by loud grunting calls. As a last resort he will fight. Another way in which males stay spread apart is by marking the edge of their territory with dung. As the animal defecates it wags its short flat tail. This scatters the dung and makes an effective scent mark.

Sometimes males are solitary, but most hippos live in groups of 10 to 15. Most hippo babies are born in the rainy season, when the grasses are growing well. Pygmy hippos live alone, or in pairs.

CAMELS AND LLAMAS

A group of six camels is huddled in the middle of the desert. It is early winter in Central Asia. The wind is blowing across the vast empty plain. There are flurries of snow. The camels' thick woolly coats are caked with snow that fell earlier. Some are sitting, with their legs tucked under their bodies. They are chewing the cud, waiting for the snowfall to stop. Then they will set off to search for patches of grass and shrubs to eat. Their double humps are plump, a sign they are still feeding well.

CAMELS AND LLAMAS Camelidae (6 species)

Size: smallest (vicuña): head-body 1.2m, shoulder height 0.91m, weight 45kg; largest (Bactrian camel): head-body 3m, shoulder height 2.1m, weight 450kg.

Colour: mainly brownish fur, but domestic forms may be white, dark or parti-coloured.

Lifespan: 20-45 years.

Species mentioned in text:
Alpaca (Lama pacos)
Arabian camel (Camelus dromedarius)
Bactrian camel (C. bactrianus)
Guanaco (Lama guanicoe)
Llama (L. glama)
Vicuña (Vicugna vicugna)

Habitat: steppe and desert. Mountain grassland.

Diet: grasses; also shrubs and salty plants (camels).

Breeding: 1 young after pregnancy of 330-410 days.

There are six species in the camel family. Wild camels still live in the Mongolian steppes. These are the two-humped Bactrian camels. Most Bactrian camels, though, are domestic animals, used to carry goods or people. Arabian (one-humped) camels are also used by people. No truly wild ones remain. They were tamed thousands of years ago. They are used by people all over northern Africa and the Middle East.

The other members of the camel family are all South American. Two are wild. The smallest is the graceful vicuña, which lives high in the Andes. The larger guanaco lives lower on the mountains, and also down to sea level on some grasslands. The other two species are the llama and alpaca. They are both domestic animals. It is believed that people bred them from the wild guanaco starting 5,000 or more years ago.

DESERT SURVIVORS

Camels are able to survive in some of the harshest deserts. They wander widely, and feed on a variety of plants. They eat thorn bushes, dry vegetation, and even saltbushes. Most animals will not eat saltbush, but camels seem to thrive better with some salty food. Camels can withstand long periods without water. They often graze far from oases, and have been known to go as long as 10 months without water. In such cases, a camel loses much weight and strength. Once it finds water, a thirsty camel may drink as much as 140 litres within a short time with no ill effects.

Camels do not store water in their bodies. They are just very good at keeping what they have got. They produce little urine, and dry faeces. They hardly sweat. Instead, they allow their body temperature to rise by as much as 8°C on a hot day, and cool down at night. This rise and fall in temperature would make most mammals ill, but not camels. Camels can sweat if they really need to. The inside of their large nose helps trap moisture rather than letting it escape from the body in the breath. Any moisture dripping from the nose runs down a groove to the split upper lip. The nostrils can be closed to keep out desert dust. The fur in the ear-flaps also keeps out dust.

KEEPING COOL

The camel's fur coat acts as insulation from the heat of the Sun. The way the camel folds its legs right under its body when it is resting cuts down the amount of surface exposed to the Sun. The camel's humps are filled with fat. This is mainly a reserve of food, as is fat in most animals, but it is concentrated on the back. Here it also serves as a barrier to the Sun's rays, without wrapping the whole camel in a layer of fat.

KEEPING WARM

Camels are not always in hot surroundings. Even in the Sahara the desert nights can be freezing. In Central Asia it can be bitterly cold all winter. The woolly coat of a camel protects it against cold. The Bactrian camel has a very thick winter coat. In spring the coat is shed in lumps, giving the animal a ragged look.

▲ **Members of the camel family** The Bactrian camel (**1**) and the Arabian camel, or dromedary (**2**) have two-toed feet with pads which spread the weight on sand or snow. The llama (**3**) has been an important beast of burden in South America for nearly 5,000 years. The alpaca (**4**) is raised for its wool. The vicuña (**5**) is from the high Andes.

HIGH LIFE

The guanaco can also live in desert conditions, but the speciality of the South American members of the camel family is living high in the mountains. The vicuña lives in alpine grasslands at 3,700 to 4,800m above sea level. The llama and the alpaca also live high in the Andes, as do some guanacos. These animals all have blood which is especially good at taking up oxygen in the thin air. They also have woolly coats that keep out the cold.

HERD LIFE

In camels and in the vicuña and guanaco, the herd usually consists of a single adult male with a harem of females. There may be 5 or 6 females in a vicuña herd, and up to 15 in a camels', plus their young. The male does not tolerate rivals, and young males are pushed out of the herd as they grow up. In the vicuña the male defends a particular area in which the herd feeds. He may stand on a mound, keeping watch on his group, and ready to give the alarm.

Camels nearly always produce a

▼With their long necks, Arabian camels feed from bushes or from the ground.

▶An alert guanaco stands on the pampas. The guanaco can often get enough water from its food without drinking. In Argentina, it is hunted for its pelt.

single baby. The newborn is able to walk and go with the herd after only a few hours. It lacks the hard pads of skin that adult camels have on their knees on which they rest on the ground. It is adult at about 5 years old. Llama and guanaco babies grow up faster. They are able to run almost the moment they are born. They feed on milk for only 3 months. Some are able to breed at 1 year old.

SPITTING AND BLOWING

All members of the camel family chew the cud. They bring the stomach contents up for a second chewing. They can also use this mechanism as defence against any animals (including people) that annoy them. Their ears go back as they bring up part of the stomach contents and spit the foul-smelling liquid over the enemy.

Male camels have another type of display which they use against rivals. In the mouth is a piece of skin which the camel can fill with air and blow out

▶Even in thin mountain air, the vicuña can run at 47kph.

like a pink balloon, at the same time giving a "roar".

VITAL AND VALUABLE

The camel family has been vital to people. All species are marvellous beasts of burden in difficult conditions. A camel can carry 100kg of luggage 30km in a day. A llama can carry a 60kg burden nearly as far, high

◄In the early morning snow, Bolivian llama drivers prepare their animals for a day of high-altitude transport. The llama may be brown, black, white or blotched. As well as carrying goods and giving wool, llamas provide meat and leather, and their dried dung is used as fuel.

in the mountains. As well as working, camels provide wool and meat. They are also milked, and can give 6 litres a day for up to 18 months. They can be ridden, raced, used in warfare, and also used as wealth.

The llama was the mainstay of the civilization of the ancient Incas. When the Spanish reached South America in the 15th century AD, over 300,000 llamas were being used in the silver mines alone. Thousands of others carried goods. The llama has good wool, but the smaller alpaca is bred especially for its wool. Some animals grow wool almost to the ground. The llama is becoming less important as a pack animal, but the alpaca is still important for wool production. There are about 3,000,000 alpacas in Peru.

The finest wool of all comes from the vicuña. However, instead of trying to conserve this valuable animal, and harvest the wool, people have killed it for a single fleece. Numbers dropped from several million in the 1500s to less than 15,000 in the late 1960s. But now the vicuña is fully protected and the population is growing again. Now there are over 80,000.

DEER

It is autumn. In a woodland glade a Red deer stag is surrounded by hinds. He lifts his head and roars. From beyond a ridge a rival replies, and then comes trotting over the hill. The two stags walk in the same direction for a while, gauging each other's size. Then they turn towards one another and their antlers clash. They push back and forth in a trial of strength. The first stag is just the stronger. The other stag breaks away and runs, but is chased by the victor.

Deer live in North and South America, Europe, North Africa, and over most of Asia including many islands. There are no deer in Africa south of the Sahara desert. Nor are there deer in Australia and New Zealand except for those introduced by people.

Deer range in size from smaller than an Alsatian dog to the moose that towers over an adult human, but most are medium-sized animals. The majority of deer are coloured in a shade of brown. Some kinds are spotted. The dull colours are good camouflage for animals such as deer which are good to eat and often hunted by others. Deer mostly feed on grasses and low-growing plants, but some kinds feed on leaves and twigs from bushes and trees. They all chew the cud.

WHAT MAKES A DEER?

Deer look similar to other plant-eaters, especially antelopes, and have graceful, elongated bodies, slender legs and necks, and short tails. They have long heads with jaws that bear many chewing teeth to deal with plant food, and also large noses providing a keen sense of smell. Their sense of hearing is also good, and the large ear-flaps are very mobile. The large round eyes are set on the side of the head, giving a good all-round view to warn of approaching enemies.

The feature which sets deer apart from all other animals, however, is the possession of a pair of antlers. These are carried only by the males (except in reindeer). Antlers are made entirely of bone, unlike the horns of cattle or antelope, which have a horny covering over a bony core. In some deer the antlers are just simple spikes. In many they are branched. The way the antlers

---

DEER Cervidae (*36 species*)

Habitat: mostly woodland and forest; some found on tundra or open grassland.

Diet: grasses, or shoots, twigs, leaves and fruit of shrubs and trees.

Breeding: 1 or 2 young after pregnancy of 24-40 weeks.

Size: smallest (pudu): head-body 0.8m, shoulder height 0.38m, weight 8kg; largest (sambar): head-body 2m, shoulder height 1.4m, weight 270kg.

Colour: mostly shades of grey, brown, red and yellow. Some adults and many young spotted.

Lifespan: 10-20 years.

Species mentioned in text:
Chital (*Axis axis*)
Fallow deer (*Dama dama*)
Indian muntjac (*Muntiacus muntjac*)
Mule or Black-tailed deer (*Odocoileus hemionus*)
Père David's deer (*Elaphurus davidiensis*)
Red brocket (*Mazama americana*)
Red deer (*Cervus elaphus*)
Reeve's muntjac (*Muntiacus reevesi*)
Roe deer (*Capreolus capreolus*)
Rusa deer (*Cervus timorensis*)
Sambar (*C. unicolor*)
Sika deer (*C. nippon*)
Swamp deer (*C. duvauceli*)
Tufted deer (*Elaphodus cephalophus*)
Wapiti (*Cervus canadensis*)
Water deer (*Hydropotes inermis*)
White-tailed deer (*Odocoileus virginianus*)

► A Red deer stag roars to lay claim to his harem. The thick neck and mane develop for the breeding season.

▼ ► American species of deer The Southern pudu (*Pudu pudu*) (1) is the smallest deer, and comes from forests in South America, as do the Red brocket (5) and the huemul (*Hippocamelus antisensis*) (4). The Swamp deer (3) is the largest South American deer and lives on wet grasslands. The Pampas deer (*Ozotoceros bezoarticus*) (2) lives on dry plains. The White-tailed deer (6) lives in small herds in North and Central America.

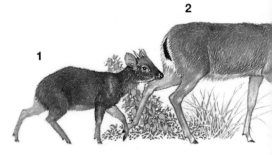

branch is slightly different for each species, so is a good means of identification. In a few species, such as the Fallow deer, the antlers have flattened sections with a hand-like (palmate) appearance.

The main function of antlers seems to be for fighting and display between the males. As males mature the antlers become bigger and, in some cases, more complicated in branching. They show well the maturity, strength and condition of a male. Thus they are good signals which another male can interpret before deciding on a challenge for supremacy.

RUTTING

In the breeding or rutting season, in species such as the Red deer and wapiti, males (stags) fight for a group or harem of females (hinds). Fights mostly take place between well-matched males. Smaller animals give up their challenge on hearing the herd master's voice or seeing his size. Fighting mainly consists of pushing matches with antlers locked, which may go on for many minutes. Losers are usually allowed to run away without harm, but sometimes bad injuries are caused by antlers. Fighting and guarding a harem takes up much energy, and males become very tired by the end of the rutting season. They need a period of rest and building up before they are again ready to mate.

RENEWABLE WEAPONS

During this rest period the antlers are shed. All deer replace the antlers regularly, unlike the permanent horns of antelope. The bone of each antler dissolves away at the base, and the antlers drop off, usually within a day or two of each other. A bony stub is left on each side of the skull. The deer begins the process of growing a new set. This involves making large amounts of new bone. Many deer gnaw cast antlers, so getting back some of the substances they need.

While the antlers are growing they are covered with skin and hair. This covering is known as "velvet". So much chemical activity goes on below the velvet that it can feel hot to the touch. When the antlers have grown to their full size for the year, the blood supply to the velvet is cut off and the skin dies and begins to shrivel. The deer may help get rid of the dead skin by rubbing its antlers against a tree.

HERDS

For much of the year typical deer live in single-sex herds. A group of females and young keep together. Males may be found singly, or else in a "bachelor herd". The intense rivalry between males occurs only in the breeding season.

The size of herds varies according to species and the habitat they live in. The Red deer is basically a woodland

▲Fallow deer prefer open woodlands. Originally from the Mediterranean, they have been introduced to Britain, and more recently to Australia.

◄Two male Black-tailed deer struggle for supremacy. Their branched antlers lock together.

►Out of the breeding season, Red deer stags live together in herds without fighting. These stags are "in velvet", in the process of growing new antlers.

animal, and there it lives in herds of about 20. In open country the herds are often larger, up to 100 strong. The chital, a deer that feeds on grass and lives in grassland and light woodland in India, may have herds of more than 100. At the other extreme is the Roe deer of Europe and Asia, and the Red brocket of South America, each of which often inhabits dense woods and forests. These deer mainly browse, eating shoots, twigs and leaves. They are solitary animals, except when breeding.

SIGNALS

Many species of deer have light-coloured rumps or tails. When the animals flee, these marks are easy for

▲ The wapiti is found in western North America and Asia. It is closely related to the Red deer, but larger. Its antlers can be more than 1m long.

others in a herd to follow. Other signals are also used. Mothers and young sometimes bleat to keep in touch with one another. Many deer "bark" when they are alarmed. Males in the breeding season can be noisy too. Their sounds range from a bellowing roar in the Red deer to a whistling scream in the Sika deer.

Deer have sensitive noses, so scent signals are especially important to these animals. Many species have special glands between the toes, which leave behind their owner's scent imprint. Glands in slits just in front of the eyes produce strong-smelling secretions. These the animals deposit on twigs and grass stems.

REARING THE YOUNG
Most deer produce a single young (calf). This stays hidden for a few weeks, emerging only when the mother visits to suckle it. After this period it moves with its mother and herd. It suckles for several months. A young deer may still be following its mother while she is rearing her next calf. Babies often have a spotted coat, but this pattern disappears long before adulthood. A few kinds of deer, including the Fallow deer, chital, and Sika deer, are spotted as adults.

The Water deer of China is unusual in that it often gives birth to triplets. Even bigger litters have been recorded. This solitary swampland deer is also unusual in having no antlers in either sex. The males have tusk-like canine teeth, as do the males of the muntjac and Tufted deer, both of which have very small antlers.

DEER AND PEOPLE
Deer have been hunted by people for their flesh (venison), skins and antlers since prehistoric times. Deer are still hunted, but in some places farms have been started to produce venison. In parts of Asia deer damage crops and are considered a pest.

Some 70 years ago, Père David's deer was nearly exterminated. This is a large species with spreading hoofs, native to the river plains of northern China. When Europeans first visited China in the 13th century, the only specimens left were in the Emperor's hunting park in Beijing. The last one there died in 1920. The species was saved because a few had been brought to Woburn in England. These bred, and now some have been taken back to China.

▲The Rusa deer of Indonesia shows the large ears, big eyes and wet nose typical of deer.

▼European and Asian species of deer The Roe deer (1) is found over much of Europe and Asia. Spotted deer include the chital (2) and Sika deer (4) from Asia. Reeve's muntjac (3), and the Tufted (5), Père David's (6) and Water deer (7) are all from Asia.

REINDEER

More than 1,000 deer trek across the flat landscape. It is spring. The animals are migrating north. Much of the time the whole herd moves at a steady trot. They come to a river, broad and flowing fast. They swim across and land downstream on the other side. On they go to the summer feeding grounds.

REINDEER
Rangifer tarandus

○　■

△ Habitat: Arctic tundra, northern woodland edges.

▨ Diet: lichens, dwarf shrubs, grasses, sedges.

◎ Breeding: 1 young after pregnancy of 210-240 days.

Size: head-body 1.2-2.2m; shoulder height to 1.3m; weight 91-272kg; males larger than females.

Colour: brown in summer, grey in winter, with white rump. White mane in rutting males.

Lifespan: 15 years.

▶This reindeer bull has just shed the velvet covering its antlers. The brow prongs (tines) which come forward over the nose can be useful in winter to brush snow off a patch of food.

Reindeer live around the edge of the Arctic, on the northern continents, and on islands such as Spitzbergen and Greenland. The same species is found all over this area, with some variation in size and colour. In America this species is known as the caribou. In Europe it is known as the reindeer. In northern Europe, Lapps tend herds of partly tame reindeer.

ALL ANTLERED

The reindeer is the only deer in which both sexes have antlers, often with palmate tops. Those of males are much larger and have more points. Females do not use their antlers to fight one another, but the antlers are useful to them in the winter for scraping through the snow to find food beneath. Reindeer also use their big feet to dig for food. The name caribou means "shovel-foot" in a Red Indian language.

MIGHTY MIGRATIONS

During the winter reindeer live at the northern edges of the woodlands bordering the Arctic. In spring they migrate far into the tree-less tundra. Here they feed on lichens and on grasses, sedges and low-growing shrubs during the brief Arctic summer when these plants grow fast. In the autumn the reindeer migrate back again to the shelter of the trees for the winter. Here they scratch a living from reindeer "moss" (a kind of lichen), and buds and shoots of shrubs.

On migration reindeer often travel in herds several thousand strong, and can cover 160km in a single day. They follow definite "trails" that have been used by the herds for many years.

▼Reindeer hoofs are broad and flat. They are good for walking on snow or soft ground. When reindeer walk their feet make a clicking sound, caused by a tendon moving over an ankle bone.

Migration routes can be 1,100km long. Wolves and other predators follow the deer on their migrations.

Not all reindeer migrate. In some areas they stay in woodland all year.

FURRY NOSES

In almost all deer the end of the nose is smooth and wet, but in the reindeer it is fur-covered. This is an adaptation to keep in body heat in Arctic conditions. The reindeer's coat has a very thick woolly underfur, guarded by longer straight hollow hairs.

Young reindeer are born during the summer. The good feeding on the summer pastures allows them to build up strength for the autumn migration and the cold of winter. It also prepares the adults for breeding. Rutting takes place in September and October. Males (bulls) may fight fiercely and gather a harem of up to 40 females (cows). After the rut the antlers fall.

PEOPLE AND REINDEER

Early in this century millions of caribou each year migrated back and forth across the tundra of North America. Now the animals are numbered in thousands rather than millions. Forest fires caused by people in the caribou's winter areas seem to be one reason for their decline.

Reindeer in Europe have been tamed for hundreds of years. The Lapps follow the herds, using them for most of their needs, including milk, meat and clothing. They mark the animals, and castrate (remove the reproductive organs of) males not needed for breeding, so cutting down fighting. But the animals roam the tundra pastures as if still wild.

◄Reindeer grazing in the tundra. Here the animals make use of the short summer season of plant growth. In 1986, as a result of the Chernobyl nuclear disaster in the USSR, tundra plants became poisonous to reindeer. Many animals died or became unfit for eating.

GIRAFFE AND OKAPI

Two female giraffes feed on a thorn tree. A kilometre away a lone male crops another tree. He is disturbed. He stops feeding and watches a movement in the distance. The females stop feeding and watch him. Uneasy, the male moves away from his tree. The females, and then three more giraffes, follow him to a safer place.

GIRAFFE AND OKAPI
Giraffidae (*2 species*)

○ ■

⬤ **Habitat:** open woodland and savannah (giraffe); dense forest (okapi).

■ **Diet:** leaves, bark and shoots. Some flowers, seeds and fruits.

◎ **Breeding:** 1 calf after pregnancy of 453-464 days.

Size: (giraffe) head-body 3.8-4.7m, height to 5.5m, weight 550-1,930kg, males larger than females; (okapi) head-body 1.9-2m, height to 1.7m, weight 210-250kg.

Colour: (giraffe) red-brown to almost black patches of variable size separated by network of lighter fur; (okapi) dark velvety purplish-brown, with white stripes on rump and legs.

Lifespan: 15-25 years.

Species mentioned in text:
Giraffe (*Giraffa camelopardalis*)
Okapi (*Okapia johnstoni*)

The giraffe family consists of two species, the giraffe and the okapi. The giraffe lives in most of Africa south of the Sahara. The okapi is found in a small area of rain forest in Zaire, but is locally common. Although a large animal, it was unknown to Europeans until 1901. Little is known of its behaviour in the wild.

The giraffe is the tallest animal. The biggest ever measured was 6.09m high to the top of the horns. The males (bulls) are heavier and much taller than the females (cows), which rarely exceed 4.5m in height.

CHOOSING DINNER
The two sexes also have different styles in eating. Male giraffes stretch up high into a tree for their food. Females more regularly feed at around their shoulder height. So not only does the giraffe feed above the level of most other animals, but the food available is divided between the sexes.

The giraffe is a browser, picking leaves and shoots off trees and shrubs. It may also eat seed pods, flowers, fruits and climbing plants. The giraffe has very mobile lips which it uses to

▲Young bull giraffes hold ritual fights to discover which is stronger. They use their necks for wrestling, and their horns and heads as butts. Only the strongest adult bulls mate with the females in an area.

▼The okapi is a secretive, solitary animal. It feeds on leaves of young tree shoots. Its face and tongue are like the giraffe's. It has poor sight, but good senses of hearing and smell.

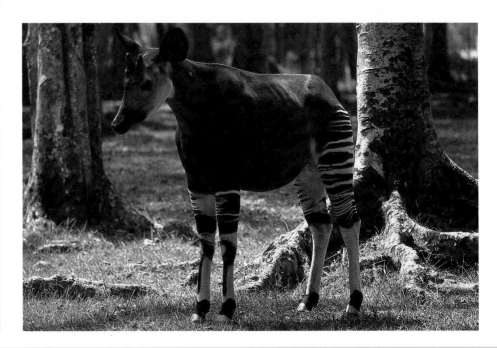

pull food to its mouth. It can stretch out its tongue about 45cm to gather food. The canine teeth are shaped like a comb, and are used to strip leaves from a branch. The animal often feeds from thorn trees, which have spines several centimetres long. It can pick leaves from between these, but will even chew thorns if they are taken into the mouth.

LONG NECK AND GIANT HOOFS

Many features of the giraffe's anatomy are very odd. Each giraffe has its own individual coat pattern, like human finger-prints. There are, though, different types of colour and pattern according to the part of Africa the giraffe lives in. The enormously long neck has only seven bones in it, like the neck of other mammals, but each one is greatly elongated. The body is comparatively short in length. Tangling the long legs is avoided by moving both legs on the same side of the body together. This produces a loping movement. When the animal raises or lowers its head, blood drains or rushes to the brain. To cope with this the blood vessels are specially elastic to help pump blood, and strong valves in the veins prevent backflow.

A giraffe is born with small horns. As it gets older, particularly if it is a bull, these grow thicker and heavier, and many bony lumps appear on the skull as well. The giraffe also has soup plate-sized hoofs. These it uses as weapons; with a powerful kick, a giraffe can kill a lion. The skin is thick and tough for defence. Adults have few enemies, but about half the young (calves) die in their first year, killed by lions, leopards or hyenas.

The giraffe has good hearing and sense of smell, but closes its nostrils when poking its head into a thorn tree. Its most acute sense, though, is sight. It can see clearly for many kilometres across the plains.

CALVING

A pregnant giraffe gives birth to her baby in a special calving area within her home range. The baby can stand soon after birth. After a week or two the calf may join up with other calves and form a "nursery group". The group is left alone during the middle of the day while the mothers go off to feed. A newborn giraffe is 1.8m tall. In its first year, it may grow 8cm a month. Giraffes are adult at about 5 years old, but males may be 8 years old before they manage to breed.

◄This male reticulated giraffe, feeding at full stretch, belongs to a race from northern Kenya and Somalia. To pump blood to its head it has a heart 60cm long and weighing more than 11kg.

WILD CATTLE

WILD CATTLE Bovidae, Tribe Bovini (*12 species*)

○ ■ ☠

△ Habitat: forest, glades, savannah, prairie.

■ Diet: grasses, other plants.

◎ Breeding: 1 calf after pregnancy of 254-340 days.

Size: smallest (Mountain anoa): head-body 1.5m, shoulder height 0.7m, weight 150kg; largest (gaur): head-body 3m, height 2m, weight to 940kg.

Colour: black, dark or reddish-brown, some with white markings.

Lifespan: 20 years.

Species mentioned in text:
African buffalo (*Syncerus caffer*)
American bison (*Bison bison*)
Banteng (*Bos javanicus*)
Domestic cattle (*B. primigenius*)
European bison (*Bison bonasus*)
Gaur (*Bos gaurus*)
Kouprey (*B. sauveli*)
Lowland anoa (*Bubalus depressicornis*)
Mountain anoa (*B. quarlesi*)
Tamarau (*B. mindorensis*)
Water buffalo (*B. arnee*)
Yak (*Bos grunniens*)

A huge shaggy brown beast emerges from a forest in eastern Europe. It is a male bison. He snorts, and clouds of water vapour come from his nostrils. He looks for a dry open patch of ground. Suddenly he lies down, and with great energy twists and rolls from side to side in the dust. He gets to his feet again and shakes himself. Then, with nostrils still steaming, he walks back in among the trees.

There are 11 species of wild cattle. Most live in Asia, Africa and Europe. Just one species, the last of the tribe, the bison (the "buffalo" of the Wild West), is found in America.

FOREST FORMS
Because domestic cattle are kept in fields of grass, it is tempting to think that wild cattle live in grasslands. In fact, most kinds of wild cattle also live in forests or woodlands, feeding on grasses in leafy glades or at forest edges. The European bison is a forest dweller that feeds on leaves, twigs and bark of trees.

The American bison lives on prairies, but could once be found in forests too. It feeds mainly on grass.

▲Yaks find enough food to live even in the snows of Tibetan mountains. Like other cattle, their food ferments in their stomachs. Heat from this (at about 40°C) provides "central heating" for the body.

◄American bison graze on grassland. In North America, European settlers slaughtered bison for meat or to deprive the local Indians of their sole means of support. Today many of the animals are protected in reserves.

FEELING FOOD

Cattle have long jaws and good chewing teeth. The end of the snout is wide, with a bare pad of skin around the lips, and large nostrils. Wild cattle have a keen sense of smell that they use to detect enemies and find food. While they are grazing, they constantly sniff the pasture to find the best fodder. Bare wet lips also provide a good sense of touch and taste, and help them find the most succulent parts of the plants. Their senses of sight and hearing are good, but not sharp.

When alarmed, cattle give an explosive snort, quickly followed by an alarm posture in which the head is held high. They face the danger with the body tensed. In the African buffalo, an alarm call may bring the whole herd to help a frightened animal.

HORNS

All the cattle are well equipped with horns. They are best developed in males, which use them to fight one another, but they are also good weapons for defence. In the African buffalo the lumps of bone to which the horns are attached make a massive ridge across the skull, and the horns meet in the mid-line, giving a helmeted appearance. A solitary buffalo may be attacked, but in a herd these animals are safe. Blind, lame or three-legged buffalo have been known to survive within the herd, and even lions are not safe from the herd's charge.

The longest horns of all are found in the Water buffalo of Asia. A specimen shot in 1955 had horns which measured 4.24m from tip to tip along the curve. Anoas and tamaraus are small species of buffalo that live in thick forest on some islands of Indonesia. They have straight, backward-pointing horns that allow them to move easily through the undergrowth.

HERDS

Little is known of the social life of these small buffalo, but in all other

The African buffalo grazes on soft grasses. There is a large dark-coloured form which is found in savannahs and open woodlands, and a smaller, redder form which is found in tropical forest.

The yak is unusual in living in grassland, tundra and ice deserts at heights of over 4,000m in Tibet. It has a dense undercoat and long shaggy dark hair to help keep out the cold.

153

species of cattle group- or herd-living is well developed. Females spend their lives in a group with other cows and their calves. Young bulls generally leave the group when about 3 years old. Forest forms such as the gaur, banteng and African forest buffalo live in groups of up to 10. Bison groups can be up to 20 strong. Groups may join up during the breeding season to form large herds. A mature bull may stay with a group through the year, or bulls may live alone or in male groups and join the cows just for mating.

In those species that live in open country, several cow groups may stay together all year. Their herds can number as many as 350 in African buffalo living on the savannah. In all cattle herds, the animals tend to do much the same thing at the same time.

FIGHTING FOR FEMALES

In the breeding season mature males keep close to females that are ready to breed, and try to keep other males away. Often they do this by threats. In American bison threats include bellowing and rolling in the dust. Approaching an opponent head-on,

◀An African buffalo displays its huge horns. When hot it goes into shade or wallows to keep cool, and may become caked with mud. The oxpeckers riding on its back pick pests from its skin.

▼Two bison bulls clash in a battle for mastery of a herd. Each can weigh 750kg and has an enormously strong head and shoulders.

or standing tall sideways on, may also warn him off.

If all else fails, the bulls fight. They slam their heads together, their hoofs churning up clouds of dust. Clumps of hair bigger than a person's fist are knocked from their heads by horns grinding against one another. The animals circle, trying to dodge lunges and drive a horn into the opponent's ribs and flank. In such a fight, one contestant may die of his wounds. But most disputes are settled peacefully.

TAME TYPES

More than one species of wild cattle has been tamed by people. The aurochs, which died out as a wild animal in 1627, was bred to produce the domestic cattle of Europe and also the zebu of the tropics, a domestic type with a hump of fat on its shoulders. The Water buffalo, too, has been tamed for thousands of years, and worked in the paddy fields of Asia. There are now many more tame Water buffalo than truly wild ones. The yak has been turned into a valuable beast of burden in the Himalayan region, and also provides milk and butter. The largest of cattle, the Asian gaur, and the smaller banteng, have also been domesticated.

The usefulness of cattle to humans is one of the main reasons why most wild species are disappearing. Land which supports them is often taken over by people to use for domestic cattle. Most endangered is the kouprey, just a few of which are left in Indo-China.

ELAND

A herd of eland lies in the shade of some bushes in the heat of the day. As the Sun's heat lessens, they get up and begin feeding. They eat the tastiest leaves, then set off to find another patch of shrubs.

The eland is one of a group of nine species of large African antelopes with spiral horns. They have some similarities to the cattle, to which they are related, but are more slender, with narrower faces. The horns corkscrew back from the top of the head.

GIANT ANTELOPES

There are two species of eland. The Common eland lives in grassland and open woodland in East, Central and southern Africa. Both sexes have horns, but they are bigger in males. The eland has a massive cow-like body, but is agile enough to jump high fences. It lives in herds that are mostly small, but in the breeding season can have 100 or more animals in them.

▼ The Four-horned antelope is a small Indian species. Only males have horns. It is a distant relation of eland and gave rise to modern cattle.

ELAND Bovidae, Tribe Strepsicorni (*9 species*); also Tribe Boselaphini (*2 species*)

○ ■

● **Habitat:** forest, open woodland and woodland edges, grassland.

■ **Diet:** leaves, fruits, flowers, seed pods, bark, tubers, grass.

◎ **Breeding:** usually 1 young after pregnancy of 245-270 days.

Size: smallest (4-horned antelope): head-body 1m, shoulder height 0.6m, weight 20kg; largest (eland): head-body 3.4m, shoulder height 1.78m, weight 950kg.

Colour: fawn, grey, or reddish-brown; striped in forest forms.

Lifespan: 15-20 years.

Species mentioned in text:
Bushbuck (*Tragelaphus scriptus*)
Common eland (*Taurotragus oryx*)
Four-horned antelope (*Tetracerus quadricornis*)
Giant eland (*Taurotragus derbianus*)
Greater kudu (*Tragelaphus strepsiceros*)
Mountain nyala (*T. buxtoni*)
Nyala (*T. angasi*)
Sitatunga (*T. spekei*)

▲Male elands "horn-tangle" to see which is strongest and will mate with the females. They thresh shrubs (1) and dig horns in mud (2), coating them with smelly mud and sap prior to fighting (3).

The herds are often found alongside giraffes or zebras. Elands wander, rather than staying in a fixed place.

The Giant eland, in spite of its name, does not differ much in size from the Common eland, but it is more a woodland species, with populations across northern Central Africa.

The other members of this group include the Greater kudu. Although males may be 1.3m at the shoulders, with horns 1.8m long, they are very graceful animals, with a bluish grey-brown coat with white vertical stripes. Females are smaller and do not have horns. The kudu likes woodland, especially in hilly regions of eastern and southern Africa.

The nyala lives in south-east Africa in dense thickets and riverside vegetation. The Mountain nyala lives on heathland and in mountain forests in some areas of Ethiopia. Once thought to be rare, it is now known to be reasonably common in these areas.

The bushbuck, the smallest of this group, is found over much of Africa where there is enough cover for it to hide in. The sitatunga is a marsh dweller. It has a shaggy oily coat, and long broad hoofs which spread its weight as it walks on mud. When alarmed, it may submerge with only its nose above water.

CHOOSY FEEDERS

The various species of spiral-horned antelope have adapted to most of the main kinds of habitat in Africa. One skill they all have is the ability to pick out the small amounts of high-quality food from the surrounding poorer-quality plants. They are browsers rather than grazers. They take fruits, seed pods, flowers, leaves, bark and tubers. Grass is a minor part of the diet of all species.

SHY ANTELOPE

Even the big herds of open-country eland are shy. The smaller antelopes of this group are mainly active during the night or at dawn and dusk. Because of this, the thick vegetation in which many live, and their shyness, they are rarely seen even where they are common.

▼The eland and its relatives have body markings, manes, beards and dewlaps that play a part in signalling.

GNU AND HARTEBEEST

As far as the eye can see across the grassland, lines of large dark animals are on the move, heading in the same direction. The animals are plodding one behind the other. Some halt a while, then once again start their trek. Altogether, there are thousands of animals. The air is filled with the sound of their soft grunts, "gnu, gnu", the sound that gives these animals their name.

Gnu can still be seen in vast herds on migration in a few parts of Africa. These animals are Brindled gnu, or wildebeest. There is another gnu species, the White-tailed gnu, but this lives in South Africa, and long ago was reduced to a tiny remnant of a few protected herds.

Related to gnu are the two species of hartebeest, and the similar hirola, topi and bontebok. All these are large antelopes. More distantly related is the medium-sized impala.

This tribe of antelopes lives mainly in fertile grasslands or woodlands of moist African savannahs. Except in the impala, both sexes grow horns. The head is long, and the body slopes from the shoulders to the hind-quarters, which makes these animals appear clumsy. Hartebeest, though,

GNU AND HARTEBEEST Bovidae, Tribe Alcelaphini (*8 species*)

○ ■ ☠

○ **Breeding**: 1 calf after pregnancy of 7-9½ months.

Size: smallest (hirola): head-body 1.2m, weight 80kg; largest (Brindled gnu): head-body 2.09m, weight 230kg.

Colour: black to grey, reddish to brown.

Lifespan: 15-20 years.

● **Habitat**: open woodland, moist savannahs.

■ **Diet**: grasses, also some leaves, flowers, fruit and seeds.

Species mentioned in text:
Bontebok (*Damaliscus dorcas*)
Brindled gnu (*Connochaetes taurinus*)
Hartebeest (*Alcelaphus buselaphus*)
Hirola (*Beatragus hunteri*)
Impala (*Aepyceros melampus*)
Topi (*Damaliscus lunatus*)
White-tailed gnu (*Connochaetes gnou*)

▼ The hartebeest lives in coarse grass-land and open woodland from West Africa to East Africa, southwards to South Africa. There are many races, each with different and characteristic horn shapes. It lives in small groups, but sometimes joins with herds of zebras or gnu.

▲Species of grazing antelope The hartebeest (1) is up to 1.3m high at the shoulders, and weighs 180kg. The impala (2) of East and southern Africa is much smaller. The bontebok (3) of South Africa is a protected species confined to special parks. The topi (4) is still widespread on the wetter savannahs. The Brindled gnu (5) puts its ear-flaps down when approaching a possible mate.

can run at speeds of up to 64kph when chased by predators.

BIZARRE ANTELOPE

With large curved horns, gnu have a face like a domestic cow, but their lean body and legs are very different. The Brindled gnu has a mane, a beard, and a long tasselled tail, all giving it an odd and rather ferocious look. Its behaviour can also be strange. If it is excited or frightened, it may paw the ground, snort, toss its head and prance about. It may run off fast, but then after a short distance turn and stare at an intruder.

In spite of its odd appearance the Brindled gnu is a successful type of antelope. It is able to live in large numbers on the savannahs from East Africa to northern South Africa. Even today, hundreds of thousands live on the plains of the Serengeti.

MIGRATING MULTITUDES

Where there is enough of the short grass it likes to feed on, the Brindled gnu may stay in the same area throughout the year. The females live in small herds. The mature males set up territories, and the adolescent males live in bachelor herds.

Where food is not always plentiful, the gnu makes migratory movements to use the best food available. At these times the animals may join together in vast moving herds. On the Serengeti Plain of northern Tanzania the gnu spreads over the open grassland during the wet season. As the dry season sets in, the animals come together on the parts that still have grass. Then they set out on a westward march to areas where there is permanent water and better grazing. The gnu travel six or seven abreast in lines that may be 10km long.

MATING ON THE MOVE

Mating takes place on the migration. As the herds briefly pause on their journey the adult males set up small territories. They try to round up a harem of females for mating. But each male may hold a territory for only a few hours before the herd is on the move again, and his band of females merges into the mass.

MEAT-EATERS' BONUS
The old, the sick and the crippled bring up the rear of the Brindled gnu herds. Hyenas, lions and other meat-eaters follow the herds and make use of the easy opportunities to catch a substantial meal.

Migrating gnu have for generations used the same trails across the central Serengeti. They carry on through many obstacles, and swim rivers in their path. In the western Serengeti they spread out again into the good pasture. Just before the rains are due they begin to move back to the open grassland of the east. They reach it about the time the rains start, and are able to feed on the flush of new grass. At about the same time, and within a week or so, the calves are born.

DANGEROUS BABYHOOD
In some years the calves are born when the herds are still on the move. The herds are still attended by hunters and scavengers, so there can be no rest for the newborn. Very quickly they have to be up on their feet and able to move with the herd. Any that are too weak or too slow will perish. A mother gnu may bravely defend her baby, but she is unlikely to be a match for a group of hyenas or African Wild dogs. Many baby gnu do not survive the first few hours. In years when the rains are late and there is little grass on which the mothers can feed, three-quarters of the calves may die.

▶ Even a flooded river does not stop the Brindled gnu on its annual migrations, although many animals may drown or die from injuries trying to cross.

ORYXES AND ADDAX

Vast expanses of sand dunes stretch in all directions. As if from nowhere come 15 white antelopes running in a group. They are addax. Their large hoofs stop them sinking and give a grip on the shifting sand. They are not running fast, but their long stride seems tireless. On they run, disappearing into the distance in search of a patch of grass.

Of all the large antelopes of Africa, the oryxes and their relations live in the driest regions. There are six species in this group.

DOOMED DESERT-DWELLERS?

The Arabian oryx used to live in the Arabian peninsula. It was only saved from extinction by breeding in captivity. The Scimitar-horned oryx lived over much of North Africa, but is now confined to a few areas and is much reduced in numbers. The addax, too,

is present in only a small part of its former range, which once included all the Sahara. These desert antelopes were once protected by living in such a harsh habitat, with few human inhabitants. When it became possible to drive vehicles into the desert, the animals became easy targets for hunters with guns, and are now in great need of conservation.

It is too late to save one antelope of this group, the bluebuck. It lived in the south-west of Cape Colony in South Africa. It was an early casualty of the spread of Europeans with their farming and firearms. It was once abundant. The last one was shot in 1800. All that is left is a few stuffed specimens in museums.

POINTED HORNS

The long straight horns of the Arabian oryx grow to 68cm long. The Scimitar-horned oryx has horns nearly twice as long, curving in an arc over its back.

ORYXES AND ADDAX Bovidae, Tribe Hippotragini (*6 species*)

○ ■ ☠

● **Habitat:** dry grassland to desert, woodland edges.

■ **Diet:** grasses, seed pods, tubers, succulents, wild melons.

○ **Breeding:** 1 calf after pregnancy of 8½-10 months.

Size: head-body 1.3-2.4m, shoulder height 0.9-1.45m, weight 65-280kg.

Colour: blackish to russet, fawn or white.

Lifespan: 20 years.

Species mentioned in text:
Addax (*Addax nasomaculatus*)
Arabian oryx (*Oryx leucoryx*)
Bluebuck (*Hippotragus leucophaeus*)
Gemsbok (*Oryx gazella*)
Roan antelope (*Hippotragus equinus*)
Sable antelope (*H. niger*)
Scimitar-horned oryx (*Oryx dammah*)

▼Arabian oryxes move to a new grazing area in the late afternoon. To survive the harsh environment, the herd needs to be highly organized. The dominant male is at the back, rounding up stragglers. A lower-ranking male leads.

◀Grazing antelope of dry regions The Roan antelope (1) and the Sable antelope (2) have long backward-curving horns. The Roan antelope is shown with its head dipping, the attitude used when giving way to superiors. The Sable antelope male pushes its horns forward to threaten another. The addax (3) has horns with a spiral twist. This male is sniffing to detect whether a female is ready to mate. The gemsbok (4) has long straight horns. The forward kick with the front leg is part of courtship.

WEARING WHITE

The desert oryxes have light-coloured or even white coats. These help to reflect the heat of the Sun. Some oryxes live where daytime temperatures may reach 50°C, so they need to keep out as much heat as possible.

Oryxes and the addax have to be able to make the best of very sparse food resources. They eat coarse grasses, and may have to obtain all the water they need from this food. They produce little urine, and if shade is available, they use it when the Sun is strongest so that little water is wasted in sweating.

The addax seems to be able to sense the presence of a patch of food from far off, perhaps by smell. The gemsbok, in addition to grasses, feeds on seed pods, wild melons and cucumbers. It also eats various tubers and bulbs that it scratches from the soil. Some of these have a high water content.

MANED ANTELOPES

The Sable and Roan antelopes have long upright manes. They are found over much of the wooded savannah country in Africa south of the Sahara, but are not common animals. They usually stay within reach of water, and cannot stand drought in the same way as oryxes. They live in herds of 4 to 20, each herd including only a single adult male. Each herd may wander over an area of up to 320 sq km during a year,

The horns end in sharp tips. Oryxes can use their horns effectively in defence. Some African tribes have used the horn tips as spearheads. The horns of all this group of antelopes have a strongly ringed appearance except at the sharp tip. Both males and females have horns.

The Beisa oryx of East Africa, which is known as the gemsbok in southern Africa, also has long, straight, pointed horns. This is the one species in the group which is still plentiful.

The biggest antelopes in the oryx group are the Sable and the Roan antelopes. These can stand 1.4m or more at the shoulders. The males are slightly larger than the females.

but in the breeding season usually stays within a circular area little more than 1km across. When the dry season comes, several herds often gather where grazing remains good, so up to 150 animals may be found together.

KEEPING APART

To a desert antelope such as oryx or addax there is little advantage in living as a big herd. Sometimes a few hundred may gather where rainstorms have started the desert vegetation growing strongly. More often, food is in short supply, and has to be searched for over a great distance. The desert antelopes live in tight little

▼ Shade is precious in the desert. The Arabian oryx spends the hottest hours under trees if it can.

groups of less than 20 animals. These include females and young, and may have more than one adult male, although the "boss" male is likely to be the one to mate with all the females. The boss male threatens the lesser males quite often, but rarely comes to blows. The sharp horns of an oryx are almost too dangerous a weapon to use against companions.

Fighting has turned into a ritual. In an oryx "tournament" the animals in the herd run around in circles, sometimes breaking into a gallop. They pace stiffly as part of the ritual, and sometimes clash horns briefly.

A VALUABLE RESOURCE

The Arabian oryx was exterminated in the wild in 1972. But a few had been gathered together in captivity in

Phoenix, Arizona, and they have been bred to continue the species. This has been successful enough for animals to be returned to Arabia. In 1982 some were released in Oman, where their progress is being watched carefully. It seems a pity that the Arabian oryx should disappear, both for its own sake, and also because it could be a useful resource. The Arabian oryx is one of the few large animals that can make a living in these difficult desert conditons. They could be useful to people for milk, meat and hides. The ancient Egyptians tamed both the addax and oryxes.

In Arabia the midday temperature can vary by as much as 45°C from summer to winter. In a single summer's day, the temperature may vary by 20°C from noon to night. Rain may

▲A male Sable antelope courts a female using a characteristic foreleg kick. In this species the mature males are black, the females brown.

▼Gemsbok, with their long pointed horns, mingle with springbok to enjoy a drink at a waterhole in the semi-desert.

not fall for years. Plants remain dormant or in seed. Sand storms can blow for days on end. The Arabian oryx can cope with all these difficulties.

CLOSE COMPANIONS

The Arabian oryx is the smallest of its group of antelopes, and needs rela-

tively little food. Its hoofs are splayed and shovel-like, with a large surface to walk on sand. It is not a great runner, but it can walk for hours on end. It is quite usual for an oryx to travel 30km in a night to find food. Because it is small, the Arabian oryx can creep into the shade under the stunted thorn trees found in parts of the desert. Unlike some antelope, it feels comfortable close to others of its own herd. The animals share tiny patches of shade.

When they feed, the herd members spread out, sometimes 100m apart. They keep looking up to see where the others are, and do not let themselves get left behind when the herd moves. An animal that gets separated from the herd can recognize and follow fresh tracks in the sand.

GAZELLES AND ANTELOPES

A herd of Thomson's gazelle are spread out on the plain. From the corner of its eye, each animal can see the black flank and twitching tail of the next. Suddenly a cheetah rushes at a gazelle at the herd's edge. The gazelle sees it and dodges away on a fast twisting run. The cheetah gives up. The rest of the herd have escaped in a series of bounds, their white rump hairs raised in alarm.

The gazelles and dwarf antelopes include 30 species. There are 18 species of gazelle which are medium-sized antelopes. Many live in dry, open country. Both sexes of most species have horns. Gazelles tend to be mainly sandy brown, fitting in well with their habitat.

The 12 species of dwarf antelope include some of the smallest hoofed mammals. Usually just the males are horned. They live in forest or in areas where there are dense thickets for cover. Gazelles are often found in herds, but dwarf antelopes live in pairs or as single animals.

TERRITORIAL MARKINGS

A dwarf antelope lives its life within a small area. It gets to know this area well and knows where to find food, shelter and escape routes from enemies. It protects this territory from other members of the same species, although a pair of antelopes may share the same territory.

Instead of fighting, dwarf antelopes keep away strangers by using scent signals. Scent glands on the hoofs leave a trail along pathways that a dwarf antelope regularly uses. Large glands in front of the eyes produce a

► Species of dwarf antelope and gazelle Klipspringer using dung to mark its territory (1). The rare beira (*Dorcatragus megalotis*) (2). The dibatag runs away with tail raised (3). Desert dwellers: Slender-horned gazelle (*Gazella leptoceros*) (4); Tibetan gazelle (5); Goitered gazelle (*G. subgutturosa*) (6); Dama gazelle, the largest gazelle (7). The oribi (8), the steenbuck (9) and Kirk's dikdik (*Madoqua kirkii*) (10), marking their territories. Royal antelope, the smallest (11). Blackbuck advancing in threat (12). A springbuck "pronks" in alarm (13).

GAZELLES AND ANTELOPES Bovidae,
Subfamily Antilopinae (*30 species*)

○ ■ ☠

● Habitat: from dense forest to desert and rocky outcrops.

■ Diet: young green leaves of bushes and grass, buds, fruit.

○ Breeding: 1 young after pregnancy of 6-8 months.

Size: smallest (Royal antelope): head-body 0.44m, weight 2kg; largest (Dama gazelle): head-body 1.72m, weight 85kg.

Colour: light brown, golden, greyish or black, usually with lighter coloured undersides.

Lifespan: 10-15 years.

Species mentioned in text:
Blackbuck (*Antilope cervicapra*)
Dama gazelle (*Gazella dama*)
Dibatag (*Ammodorcas clarkei*)
Dorcas gazelle (*Gazella dorcas*)
Gerenuk (*Litocranius walleri*)
Günther's dikdik (*Madoqua guentheri*)
Klipspringer (*Oreotragus oreotragus*)
Mongolian gazelle (*Procapra gutturosa*)
Oribi (*Ourebia ourebi*)
Pygmy antelope (*Neotragus batesi*)
Royal antelope (*N. pygmaeus*)
Springbuck (*Antidorcas marsupialis*)
Steenbuck (*Raphicerus campestris*)
Suni (*Neotragus moschatus*)
Thomson's gazelle (*Gazella thomsoni*)
Tibetan gazelle (*Procapra picticaudata*)

◀A male Kirk's dikdik has straight spiked horns. In front of the eye is the large gland used in scent marking. The snout is long, overhanging the bottom lip.

▼The male gerenuk, but not the female, has horns. Here a pair are courting. The male displays by turning the head sideways (1), then places scent from the gland in front of his eye on the female's rump (2). He taps the female with his foreleg (3) and sniffs her (4) before deciding whether she is ready to mate.

sticky secretion which the dwarf antelope wipes on to twigs and stems to help mark its territory. It also deposits dung and urine at particular sites, producing another scent marker. Both sexes add to the pile, a male adding his dung to a female's.

These markers usually repel possible intruders without a fight. One type of dwarf antelope, the dikdik, also threatens other males by "horning" (scratching at vegetation with its horns) and raising a crest of longer hairs on its head.

NOURISHING DIET

Most dwarf antelopes feed on the best parts of the vegetation around. They do not graze on old tough grass, but browse on bushes, taking the young green leaves. They eat buds, fruit and some fallen leaves and may pick tender new shoots of grass. Many of them thrive in places where the original vegetation has been disturbed by people and new vegetation is sprouting. This kind of food is packed full of nourishment.

SMALL AND CUNNING

The Royal antelope of West Africa competes with the chevrotains for title of smallest hoofed mammal. It is certainly the smallest horned mammal. It is shy and secretive, living in pairs in the thickest of forest. The Pygmy antelope of Central Africa and the suni of East Africa are almost as small and also live in forest with thick undergrowth.

All these have an arched back and short neck, which are useful for getting through the tangled growth. Female dwarf antelopes are usually a little larger than the males. In the folk-stories of several African countries dwarf antelopes have a reputation for cunning which makes up for their lack of size.

NOSE COOLERS

The three species of dikdik live in Africa in dry country with scrub and thorn bushes. They pair for life and are usually seen in pairs. Dikdiks, especially Günther's dikdik, have a long, rather fleshy nose. Water evaporates from the inside lining of this to help cool the animals down. Sometimes they pant through their noses. The name "dikdik" imitates the sound of the alarm cry they give as they dash away from danger.

The steenbuck and two species of grysbuck live in African woodland in the east and south. They are rather solitary and have large home ranges. The oribi is the tallest of the dwarf antelopes, up to 67cm high at the shoulders. It lives on grassy plains near water and, unusually for this group, eats grass.

ROCK JUMPER

The oddest dwarf antelope is the klipspringer. It lives in Africa in areas where there are dry rocky outcrops. It moves with a bouncing gait, and can arch its back to stand with all four feet together to balance on a tiny patch of level rock. It stands on the tips of its small round hoofs. Each hoof has a rubbery centre and a hard outer ring, making a good pad to grip the rocks.

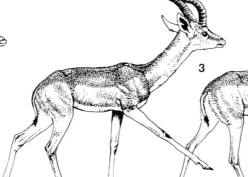

The hair is thick, bristly, light and hollow-shafted. It keeps the klipspringer warm and also makes a buffer to cushion the body from knocks on the rock.

CAMOUFLAGE IN THE OPEN

The gazelles live in a more open habitat than the dwarf antelopes. Most species have coats that are fawn above and pale beneath. This colouring helps their camouflage by disguising the shadows of an animal standing in the open. Some gazelles, such as the springbuck, have a black band along the side. This may also camouflage the animal by helping to break up the outline.

At close quarters such markings, and coloured tails and rump patches, can work as signals between herd members. Gazelles have good hearing and eyesight. Smell seems less important to these animals.

The different species of gazelle live from southern Africa north to the Mediterranean, and across Arabia to India and China. In North Africa and Asia they live in dry or desert regions. Here their numbers are low and their populations are rather scattered.

MARCHING MILLIONS

Some gazelles live singly, but most form herds – although these are often little more than family groups. Large numbers of Thomson's gazelle live in East Africa, sometimes forming herds of up to 200. Thousands may come together when migrating to areas of fresher grass.

In the past the biggest herds were those of the springbuck of southern Africa on migration. Herds of millions formed, taking several days to pass a given point. Most were killed as a nuisance to farming. Now few springbuck are left, and their migrations are a thing of the past.

The blackbuck lives across the Indian subcontinent, in areas ranging from semi-desert to light woodland. It

▶The typical stance of fighting gazelles is shown by these Thomson's gazelles. Their heads are as close to the ground as possible, with the strongly ringed horns interlocked.

▼The gerenuk lives singly or in small groups. It is unique among antelopes in its ability to stand on its hind legs at full stretch to feed and to walk round a tree in this position.

is unique among gazelles in that the male is a different colour to the female. A breeding male has a black back while the female has the usual gazelle brown. The male's colour develops as it matures. It also has long spiral horns – the female has none.

A strong male blackbuck gathers a herd of up to 50 females and young in the breeding season. He threatens other males by lifting his head and tail and dropping his ears. Only rarely do threats lead to fights. The blackbuck is a strong runner, faster than almost any animal except the cheetah.

DESERT AND GRASSLAND

The Dorcas gazelle is a small species about 60cm tall, but able to run at almost 80kph. Youngsters are able to keep up with their mother within a week or two of birth. The Dorcas gazelle is found in scattered pockets

from Morocco to India in flat stony desert. It varies in size, coat colour and horn shape through this range.

On the steppes and high plateaux of Central Asia live the Tibetan and Mongolian gazelles. Only the males of these species have horns. In Tibet, gazelles live as high as 5,500m. Herds of Mongolian gazelles migrate across the grasslands to the summer pastures. Migrating herds may contain 8,000 animals. In the rutting season the males have swollen throats.

GIRAFFE GAZELLES

Two kinds of gazelle in Africa have very long necks and in their shape and habits are like giraffes. The dibatag is the smaller of the two, about 80cm tall at the shoulders, and lives in Somalia. It lives in scrub desert with scattered thorn bushes and grass. The gerenuk is bigger, up to 1m tall, with an even longer neck than the dibatag. It lives from Ethiopia south to Tanzania in desert and dry bush savannah.

The feeding habits of these gazelles are like the giraffe's. They pick tender leaves and shoots from thorn bushes and other bushes and trees, also eating some flowers and fruits. They do not eat grass. Their narrow muzzles and mobile lips help them pick the tasty morsels from among the thorns.

To reach enough food, the gerenuk often stands on its hind legs and stretches upwards. Its diet varies between the rainy and dry seasons as the availability of different plant species changes too. In Tsavo National Park, Kenya, more than 80 plant species are eaten during the year. Some plants are evergreens, with thick hard leaves coated with a waxy layer that prevents evaporation of water. This allows the gerenuk to inhabit very dry areas.

▲A cheetah has pulled down and killed a Thomson's gazelle. Few other animals are fast enough to catch an adult gazelle unless it is taken completely unaware, but young babies are vulnerable.

GOATS AND SHEEP

High in the Rocky Mountains two horned male sheep face one another. These rams stand a little apart, lower their heads slowly, then rush at each other. They crash into one another head-on, with an enormous bang that echoes round the mountain. They back away, then launch themselves again, banging their enormous horns together with a jarring crash. Again and again they do this, until one accepts defeat and retreats. Neither animal has been injured by this head-banging.

Although it is easy to tell a domestic sheep from a domestic goat, it is not always so easy with the wild species. Females may be very similar. Males show more differences. In goats the males have chin beards and usually smell strongly. Goats have anal scent glands, and the males may also spray themselves with urine. Males have sharp scimitar-shaped horns with knobbed ridges. Goats have long flat tails with a bare underside.

Male sheep do not have chin beards but may have a throat mane. Sheep, unlike goats, have scent glands between the toes, in the groin and in front of the eye, but no anal gland. Male sheep (rams) do not have the offensive smell of goats. Rams have large, rather blunt horns which curl in a spiral. Sheep have short tails and often have a rump patch.

AGILE CLIMBERS

Goats and sheep tend to live in different types of country. Goats specialize in cliffs, while sheep live in the open, rolling dry lands close to cliffs. But both types of animal include agile climbers. This group of animals has made use of some of the most difficult, dangerous land, and eats

GOATS AND SHEEP
Bovidae; tribes Caprini, Rupicaprini, Saigini (*24 species*)

Habitat: often steep terrain, from hot desert and moist jungle to snowy wastes.

Diet: grasses, leaves and bark of shrubs, other plants.

Breeding: 1 or 2 lambs or kids after pregnancy of 150-180 days.

Size: head-tail 1.1-1.86m, weight 25-140kg.

Colour: usually shade of brown, some blackish, white or golden.

Lifespan: 10-15 years.

Species mentioned in text:
Argalis (*Ovis ammon*)
Barbary sheep (*Ammotragus lervia*)
Bighorn sheep (*Ovis canadensis*)
Chamois (*Rupicapra rupicapra*)
Chiru (*Pantholops hodgsoni*)
Goral (*Nemorhaedus goral*)
Himalayan tahr (*Hemitragus jemlahicus*)
Ibex (*Capra ibex*)
Japanese serow (*Capricornis crispus*)
Mainland serow (*C. sumatrensis*)
Markhor (*Capra falconeri*)
Mouflon (*Ovis musimon*)
Mountain goat (*Oreamnos americanus*)
Saiga (*Saiga tatarica*)
Snow sheep (*Ovis nivicola*)
Thinhorn sheep (*O. dalli*)
Wild goat (*Capra aegagrus*)

▼▶**Goats or goat antelopes** Goral (1), Japanese serow (6), chamois (7) and Mountain goat (9) have both sexes similar in size and looks. They have short, sharp horns. In many other species males are bigger and have beards and manes. A male Himalayan tahr (2) may weigh 108kg. The male urial (*Ovis orientalis*) (3) and male Barbary sheep(4) have spiral horns and a throat mane. The Wild goat (5) and ibex (8) have long curved horns. The argalis (10) has huge horns.

▲The Mountain goat has a thick coat with a layer of fat beneath to keep it warm in bitter cold.

some of the toughest plants.

There are 24 species of goats and their relatives. Some are rather odd looking, such as the serows, chamois, goral and Mountain goat. More "typical" in appearance are the tahrs and the true sheep and goats. There are also two bigger species of "giant goat", the Musk ox and takin.

SIMILAR TO GAZELLES

On the borderline between the goats and the gazelles are two species, the saiga and the chiru. The chiru lives high in the plateaux of Tibet in small groups. Only the male has horns. The same is true of the saiga. This animal once lived across a wide area, from Poland to the steppes of Central Asia, in large numbers. It was hunted to near extinction, but is now protected and out of danger.

The saiga migrates long distances across the steppes, and huge herds form at this time. The saiga is a fast runner, reaching speeds of up to 60kph. It has a large bulbous nose, which helps to warm the air it breathes. It also has a good sense of smell.

The chiru and saiga look and behave like gazelles, and this is what the majority of scientists now believe them to be.

STURDY AND SURE-FOOTED

The serows are rather clumsy and slow compared to goats, but they are sure-footed as they go up and down the steep rocky slopes of their home areas. They live where there is shrub or tree cover. The Mainland serow is found from India south to Sumatra and east to southern China. The Japanese serow is found in much cooler conditions, including snow, in Japan and Taiwan. Both species of serow are browsers.

The goral is a smaller but similarly shaped animal, with a slightly shaggy coat, living over a wide area of Asia from India to Thailand and north to Siberia. It usually lives in dry climates on very steep cliffs. The goral climbs and jumps well. It feeds morning and evening and may rest on a sunny ledge for much of the day.

GOATS OF THE SNOWS

The Mountain goat lives in western North America. It is found in rocky areas high in the mountains, often above the tree line. It climbs steep cliffs and along the edges of large glaciers. The Mountain goat is sure-footed, but moves slowly most of the time. It eats grasses and lichens and

▼A domestic sheep cleans her new-born lamb. The domestic sheep's dense woolly coat is not found in wild sheep.

▶A group of Thinhorn sheep stay alert as they rest and chew the cud on a pasture high in the mountains of Alaska.

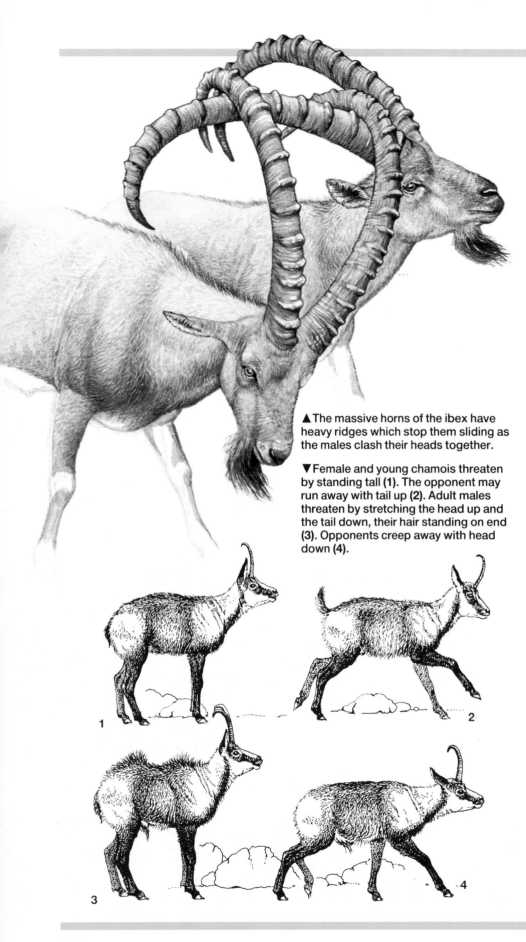

▲The massive horns of the ibex have heavy ridges which stop them sliding as the males clash their heads together.

▼Female and young chamois threaten by standing tall (1). The opponent may run away with tail up (2). Adult males threaten by stretching the head up and the tail down, their hair standing on end (3). Opponents creep away with head down (4).

may browse on bushes. Because it lives where the snowfall is heavy, the Mountain goat has developed a stocky build and a thick white woolly coat. The thick legs look as though they are in pantaloons. They have very large hoofs with hard rims and softer centres which give a good grip.

The most nimble of the "near-goats" is the chamois. This lives in the cold snowy mountains of Europe and Asia Minor. The chamois comes down the mountain to spend winter in woodland, where it feeds on buds, young tree shoots, lichens and small grass patches. Summer is spent high on the mountains, feeding on grasses and herbs.

The chamois can make use of tiny areas of good footing to leap up and down the most unlikely looking rock faces at speed. A whole herd will throw itself down a cliff which, to a human, looks almost impossible to climb. Even the babies are agile. The kids are born in May and June on rocky, inaccessible areas. They can follow their mother almost immediately, and within a week are at home jumping about the crags.

Old male chamois are usually solitary, but females live in herds of up to 30. Males fight viciously during the breeding season, using their hooked horns. Unless a loser submits by flattening himself on the ground, he may be gored to death.

BEARDLESS GOATS

Tahrs live on tree-covered mountain slopes and cliffs. They have no beards and a naked muzzle. The horns are rather flattened. Males do not smell like true goats. The Himalayan tahr has a thick shaggy mane around its shoulders. Other species live in southern India and in Oman. Tahrs are wary animals. A few animals in the herd of up to 40 are always on watch.

The Barbary sheep is native to North Africa. It is found in mountainous areas which are barren and rocky.

It seems able to survive without drinking water. In some respects it is more like a goat than a sheep, and it has a long flat tail. But it fights like a sheep, by clashing heads together. The horns of big male Barbary sheep are large. Males also have a body weight twice that of females.

TRUE GOATS

Six species of wild goat are found from the Pyrenees to central China. They are mainly browsers, but also graze. The ibex exists in a number of slightly different forms in various mountain ranges. The horns of the Siberian ibex are the longest, growing to 1.4m.

The horns of the markhor grow equally long, but they are twisted. The markhor lives in the mountains of Central Asia and is the largest goat. Males can be 1m high at the shoulders and weigh 110kg.

The Wild goat from which our domestic animals were bred still exists in western Asia and the eastern Mediterranean. It was first tamed in western Asia approximately 8,500 years ago. Its eating habits prevent the regrowth of trees in some parts of the world.

GRAZING IN HERDS

Six species of sheep live from the Mediterranean across Asia to Siberia and in the west of North America. Most live by grazing. They are herd animals which rely on keeping together to escape enemies.

The mouflon is a small sheep found in Asia Minor and the Mediterranean. This is probably the species from which tame sheep were bred. Some of the old-fashioned breeds like the St Kilda sheep still have much the same size and colouring as the mouflon. It is chestnut brown with a light saddle. The mouflon is hardy and can live in cold or desert habitats. Domestic sheep have been bred for various characters, including a long woolly fleece, and there are now many breeds, mostly with white coats.

MOUNTAIN SHEEP

The largest wild sheep is the argalis, which lives in cold desert and mountain habitats in Central Asia. It has a light brown coat with a white rump patch. A male can be 1.25m tall and weigh 180kg. The horns curve in a spiral and can be 1.9m long and 50cm round, weighing up to 22kg.

The Snow sheep lives in the mountains and Arctic wastes of Siberia. The Thinhorn sheep lives in similar conditions in Alaska and western Canada. The Bighorn lives in mountainous and dry desert areas from Canada to Mexico. In the Rocky Mountains it occupies the same areas as the Mountain goat, yet the two species have very different life-styles. The Bighorn is migratory, moving seasonally across wide areas of woodland, while the Mountain goat ruthlessly defends a territory when food becomes scarce on the cliffs in deep snow.

▼The chamois moves lower down the slopes in the winter, but is still likely to encounter snow in its mountain home. These animals are at 2,100m in the Swiss Alps.

MUSK OX AND TAKIN

It is the middle of the Arctic winter. Although it is permanent night, light from the Moon comes out of a clear sky. The wind whips across the open landscape and the temperature is −60°C, colder than most food freezers. A small group of Musk ox are feeding, scraping with their hoofs at the thin snow cover. Under the snow are frozen lichens and other low plants. The animals eat them silently, taking no notice of the bitter cold.

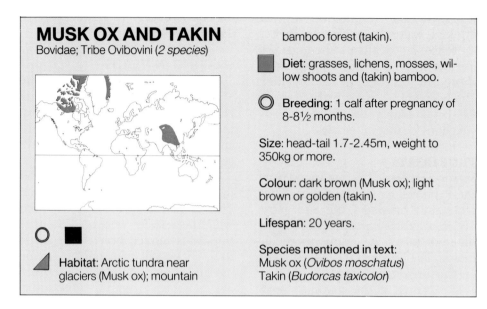

MUSK OX AND TAKIN
Bovidae; Tribe Ovibovini (*2 species*)

Habitat: Arctic tundra near glaciers (Musk ox); mountain bamboo forest (takin).

Diet: grasses, lichens, mosses, willow shoots and (takin) bamboo.

Breeding: 1 calf after pregnancy of 8-8½ months.

Size: head-tail 1.7-2.45m, weight to 350kg or more.

Colour: dark brown (Musk ox); light brown or golden (takin).

Lifespan: 20 years.

Species mentioned in text:
Musk ox (*Ovibos moschatus*)
Takin (*Budorcas taxicolor*)

The Musk ox is more closely related to goats than to cattle. Its closest relative of all is the takin. The takin lives in a temperate climate in China and Burma. The Musk ox, though, lives in the bitterest climate of any mammal, in the high Arctic of North America and on Greenland.

GROUND-LENGTH COAT
The coat of the Musk ox has two parts. The inner coat is soft, very fine and light. It is so thick that cold does not penetrate. Growing through this there are long guard hairs, forming a long overcoat which reaches nearly to the ground. Individual hairs may be as much as 60cm or more long.

This outer coat can shrug off snow and rain and keeps out the wind. It takes the wear and tear, so that the Musk ox's warmth-giving inner coat stays in good working order. In early summer the inner coat is shed and replaced. The compact shape of the

▲ The takin lives in the highest bamboo forests and rhododendron thickets. It eats grasses and bamboo shoots.

▼ The Musk ox huddles in steaming groups for warmth. They are the only large mammals to spend all year on the treeless Arctic tundra.

Musk ox, with its short legs, neck and tail, also helps it retain heat.

The Musk ox's coat makes it look bulky, but it runs well. It is able to turn and wheel at surprising speed.

SEX DIFFERENCES

During the rut the bulls produce a secretion from glands just in front of the eye. They fight each other by running together and banging their heads, making a noise that can be heard more than a kilometre away.

The horns form a helmet over the top of the skull, nearly joining in the midline. They curve down, then out. The part of the horn on top of the skull may be over 20cm thick in a big male, making a cushion for crashing skulls.

Females have horns too, but they are smaller. A female Musk ox weighs little over half the male's weight.

PROTECTIVE BUNCH

The Musk ox is a social animal and lives in herds. Often a herd has only

about 12 animals, but there can be as many as 100. They stay in a close bunch for protection against enemies and bad weather.

In summer the Musk ox feeds well on the tundra, on grasses and dwarf shrubs. It builds up a layer of fat which protects it from cold and starvation in the winter. The Musk ox can survive only in areas where the snow cover is not deep enough to bury the food out of reach.

The Musk ox calf is born in May. Even then the temperature can be well below freezing, and it has a thick woolly coat. It is about 45cm tall and after an hour can follow its mother.

▼ When threatened by enemies, a herd of Musk ox form a line facing them, or a circle with the calves in the middle. Big males dash out and jab with their horns. This is a good defence against wolves, but not against people with guns.

▼ The takin needs much less fur than the Musk ox, but it has a heavy body and large hoofs. Some races are golden in colour. Most are light coloured, with dark faces in bulls. The takin's skin secretes a strong smelling grease.

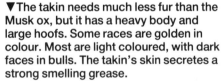

AARDVARK

The Sun has set over the sparsely wooded grassland. Dotted here and there, nearly as tall as the trees, are the great mounds of termite nests. An animal the size of a pig makes its way in a zigzag path towards one of the mounds. It is an aardvark on its way to feed. A hole at the base of the mound shows it has been there before. It sets to work again, snout close to the ground, digging swiftly. It makes good progress, even though the mound is rock hard. From time to time the aardvark pauses, sits down and thrusts its snout into the mound to feed on the insects scurrying about inside.

◄An aardvark sits down by a termite mound ready to feed at night. Termites in the wet season and ants in the dry season are its favourite foods.

▼In parts of Zaire, people kill aardvarks both for food and for their hair and teeth. The hair is crushed into a powder and used as a poison. The teeth are used as good-luck charms.

Aardvarks are found in most parts of Africa south of the Sahara desert. But they avoid the driest desert regions and the depths of the tropical rain forest. The name aardvark means "earth pig" in the Afrikaans language, and the animal does look rather like a pig, although it is no relation. It has a long round snout, big ears and a bristly coat.

The aardvark eats ants and termites, but it is not related to anteaters. In fact it is not closely related to any other mammal. Its nearest relatives appear to be hyraxes and elephants. It has certain body features in common with these animals – for example, their claws are a cross between nails and hoofs. For this reason they are sometimes classed together as "primitive ungulates". Ungulates are the hoofed mammals.

THICK-SKINNED AND SHY

The aardvark eats ants and termites using its long, worm-like tongue, which is sticky with saliva. Its skin is thick and tough, which protects it from insect bites.

The aardvark has keen hearing and a well-developed sense of smell, senses it uses when foraging for food. A mat of hair around the nostrils helps keep out the dust. The animal can also close its nostrils when digging to prevent dirt and insects getting in.

Aardvarks are shy and secretive creatures, whose way of life is not well known. They spend the day asleep in a tunnel-like burrow. They dig several burrows within the home territory and may rest in a number of them during the night.

The young are born in a deeper and longer burrow system. They emerge above ground after about 2 weeks and go out foraging with their mother. They begin to dig their own burrows at 6 months old, but usually stay with the mother until she mates again.

AARDVARK
Orycteropus afer

● ■

▲ Habitat: open woodland, scrub and grassland.

■ Diet: ants and termites, sometimes fruit.

◎ Breeding: 1 young born after pregnancy of about 7 months.

Size: head-body 105-130cm; tail 45-63cm; weight 40-65kg.

Colour: yellowish-grey coat, head and tail off-white, often stained brownish by soil.

Lifespan: up to 10 years in captivity.

PANGOLINS

Two lion cubs are padding through the grassy savannah. They spy a curious scaly creature shuffling along in front of them. It is a pangolin. When it hears them coming, the pangolin rears up on its hind legs and starts running. Its long tail acts like a prop to help it stay upright.

The pangolin has been described as a "walking pine-cone" or "walking artichoke" because of the overlapping scales that cover all except the underside of its body. Its favourite foods are ants and termites. It has no teeth, but grinds up the insects with the hard lining of its stomach.

THE TREE PANGOLINS

Pangolins live in Africa and Asia, in the dense tropical rain forests and in the more open grasslands. They are active mainly at night. The African rain forests are home for two species of pangolin which stay mainly in the trees.

The Long-tailed pangolin spends most of its time high up in the forest canopy. It feeds from nests of ants and termites hanging from the branches. The larger Small-scaled tree pangolin keeps more to the lower branches of the trees. Both species have a long

▲A Small-scaled tree pangolin. Pangolins' overlapping brown scales give them an unusual appearance.

▼A Cape pangolin drinks at the Etosha National Park in Namibia. Outside such parks, people hunt pangolins widely for their meat and scales.

PANGOLINS Manidae
(*7 species*)

● ◾ 🐾

◨ **Habitat:** wide range, from forest to open savannah.

▦ **Diet:** mainly ants and termites.

◎ **Breeding:** usually 1 offspring after pregnancy of 4½ months (Cape pangolin).

Size: smallest (Long-tailed pangolin): head-body 30cm, tail 55cm, weight 1.2kg; largest (Giant pangolin): head-body 85cm, tail 80cm, weight 33kg.

Colour: light yellowish-brown, through olive to dark brown, with white to brown undersurface hair.

Lifespan: up to 13 years in captivity (Indian pangolin).

Species mentioned in text:
Cape pangolin (*Manis temmincki*)
Chinese pangolin (*M. pentadactyla*)
Giant pangolin (*M. gigantea*)
Indian pangolin (*M. crassicaudata*)
Long-tailed pangolin (*M. tetradactyla*)
Malayan pangolin (*M. javanica*)
Small-scaled tree pangolin
 (*M. tricuspis*)

prehensile tail, with a sensitive bare patch at the tip which helps them climb.

THE GROUND DWELLERS
The two other African species of pangolin are bigger still and they are ground dwellers. They are the Cape pangolin and Giant pangolin. They use their powerful foreclaws to destroy termite mounds and ants' nests and then take up the insects with their long tongues, which are covered with sticky saliva. The Giant pangolin has an unusually long tongue – up to 70cm. It may eat as many as 200,000 ants in a single night.

The pangolins of Asia are natives of central and southern India, southern China and as far south as Malaysia and the Indonesian islands. The name pangolin comes from a Malay word meaning "rolling over", which is what pangolins do when threatened.

The three species of Asian pangolin, that is the Indian, Chinese and Malayan pangolins, are similar in appearance. They live mainly on the ground but can climb skilfully. They differ from their African relatives in having hair at the base of their scales.

SMELLS AND SPRAYS
Pangolins live for most of the time alone. Their main sense is that of smell. They mark their territory with their droppings and urine and with a foul-smelling liquid from glands at the base of their tail.

They will also spray this liquid and urine in the face of animals that attack them. The larger ones may also lash out at their attackers with their tail. But pangolins usually rely on curling into a ball for defence. The overlapping scales on its body form a shield that is impregnable to all but the larger cats and hyenas.

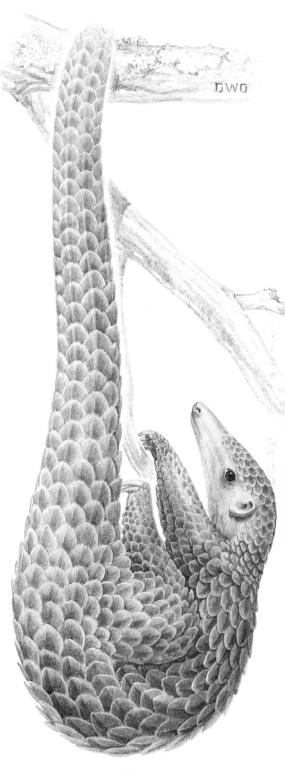

▲A Small-scaled tree pangolin hangs by its tail from a branch. The tail has a short bare patch at the tip to make gripping easier.

BEAVERS

The crisp morning air echoes to the sound of chiselling as a beaver gnaws away at the trunk of a young tree. The tree grows thinner and thinner at the base until it snaps and crashes to the ground. Grasping the trunk in its powerful jaws, the beaver drags it to the water's edge and dives in. The tree is pushed and pulled into position in the sprawling mound of branches, twigs and mud which makes up the beaver's dam.

Beavers are rodents which have become adapted to living in water. Their thick fur is waterproofed with grease, while their hind feet are webbed for swimming. When beavers dive, their ears and nostrils close, and a membrane covers their eyes. The throat becomes blocked off by the tongue to prevent water filling the lungs.

Beavers swim using an up-and-down action of their broad flat tail to give extra force against the water. On land, they are much less agile. They have a clumsy, shuffling walk.

UNIQUE DAM-BUILDERS
The dam-building activity of beavers is unique in the animal world. Large branches or tree trunks form the framework of the dam, while the beavers pack sticks, stones and mud into place around them. This solid unit holds back river water so that it

▲ This North American female beaver is carrying her kit through the water using her large teeth and front feet.

▼ The Mountain beaver does not build dams. It lives in underground burrows in coniferous forests.

BEAVERS Castoridae and Aplodontidae (*3 species*)

● ■

◢ Habitat: swamp near lakes and streams.

■ Diet: leaves, herbs, grasses, woody stems.

○ Breeding: litters of 1–8 after pregnancy of 105 days.

Size: head-body 80-120cm; weight 11-30kg.

Colour: reddish-brown, sometimes darker.

Lifespan: 10-15 years.

Species mentioned in text:
European beaver (*Castor fiber*)
Mountain beaver (*Aplodontia rufa*)
North American or Canadian beaver (*Castor canadensis*)

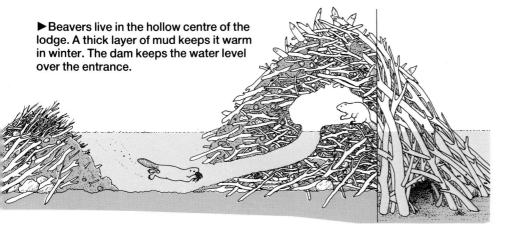

►Beavers live in the hollow centre of the lodge. A thick layer of mud keeps it warm in winter. The dam keeps the water level over the entrance.

years, and both help to raise the young. They produce one litter each spring consisting of several kits. These are born covered in fur, able to swim and with their eyes open, but they do not leave the lodge until they are weaned at 6 weeks. The young beavers born the previous year help their parents to look after the kits, bringing fresh leaves to the lodge. They leave the family unit in their second year to start their own lodges.

TRAPPED IN THOUSANDS

Beaver skins are highly prized for making coats and hats because they are warm and waterproof. Thousands of beavers are trapped in Russia, America and Europe every year. They have almost been wiped out in the past by over-hunting. The European beaver is now found only in small isolated populations.

spreads out to form a deep pond.

Beavers are vegetarians, and in autumn they gather and store woody plant material in the pond. The cold temperature stops decay organisms attacking the material. The beavers rely on it for food throughout the winter. In spring and summer, when there is a greater choice of food,

beavers change to a diet of soft leaves.

The beaver's living quarters or lodge is usually built in deep water behind the dam. It is also built of mud and branches. The entrance is under water to prevent enemies getting in, and it leads to a central chamber.

Male and female beavers stay together as a mating pair for several

◄By creating deep ponds, beaver dams cause important changes in the local habitat.

▲Beavers use scent to mark their territory, so they have extremely sensitive noses.

SQUIRRELS

The Sun rises over the dry plains of central North America. The inhabitants of a small colony are already awake, preparing for the day ahead. Suddenly a male spots a puma and he barks out a warning. His companions dash back into their homes, while he stands erect on a look-out mound, keeping watch as he cleans his whiskers. This is, of course, not a human town. About 2,000 Black-tailed prairie dogs live here, in burrows under the short, dry grass.

All squirrel species grip small items of food firmly in their forepaws, like the Cape ground squirrel (above left). The

European red squirrel leaves many feeding signs (above right) as it opens cones and nuts to extract the seeds.

It may seem odd to think of squirrels living underground rather than in trees. But the burrowing prairie dogs are just some of the members of the very numerous and widespread squirrel family. This family includes the familiar Grey and European red squirrels and other tree-dwelling species, the flying squirrels and the ground-dwelling prairie dogs, chipmunks, ground squirrels and sousliks.

Squirrels, being so variable in their way of life and habits, are found in many different types of country – from mountain meadow to rocky cliff, dry grassland and tropical rain forest. Members of the family are found on every continent except Australia and Antarctica.

THE SQUIRREL'S MENU

A typical squirrel has a long rounded body, large eyes, strong legs and claws and a bushy tail. The long, chisel-shaped front teeth show that they are members of the rodent group. These teeth are well suited for chopping and opening nuts and seeds, snipping off flowers, fruits and shoots and levering strips of sappy bark from a tree trunk. Plant food is the main diet of most types of squirrel, as well as mushrooms and other fungi.

▶ The European red squirrel is many people's idea of a typical squirrel, with its large eyes, pricked ears and long, bushy tail.

SQUIRRELS Sciuridae (*267 species*)

● ◨

◨ Habitat: tropical forest to woods, grassland and gardens.

■ Diet: plant parts such as seeds, nuts, bark; some small animals.

○ Breeding: most species have one spring litter after pregnancy of 3-6 weeks; number of young varies: 1 or 2 (flying squirrels) to 9 or more (Grey squirrel).

Size: smallest (African pygmy squirrel): head-body 7cm, tail 5cm, weight 10g; largest (Alpine marmot): head-body 73cm, tail 16cm, weight 8kg.

Colour: shades of red, brown or grey.

Lifespan: 1-2 years in smaller species, 8-10 years for some marmots.

Species mentioned in text:
African pygmy squirrel (*Myosciurus pumilio*)
Alpine marmot (*Marmota marmota*)
Belding's ground squirrel (*Spermophilus beldingi*)
Black-tailed prairie dog (*Cynomys ludovicianus*)
Cape ground squirrel (*Xerus inaurus*)
European red squirrel (*Sciurus vulgaris*)
Giant flying squirrel (*Petaurista* species)
Grey squirrel (*Sciurus carolinensis*)
Shrew-faced ground squirrel (*Rhinosciurus laticaudatus*)
Siberian chipmunk (*Tamias sibiricus*)
Woodchuck (*Marmota monax*)

One of the reasons for the squirrels' success is their broad diet. Many species eat beetles or other insects. Some are omnivorous, and their diet includes lizards, small birds, eggs and worms as well as plant food. The Shrew-faced ground squirrel is unusual in that it mostly eats insects, such as termites and caterpillars.

LEAPING AND GLIDING

Tree squirrels are very agile animals. They can run straight up or down a tree trunk and leap several metres through the branches, clinging with their sharp claws. They have keen sight, which helps them judge distances accurately when scampering among the twigs.

Flying squirrels are specialized not for true flying but for gliding. There is a furred flap of skin down each side of the body, stretching between the front and back legs. As the flying squirrel jumps, it extends all four legs to stretch the skin and form a parachute. The tail is free to move from side to side, like a rudder for steering.

Flying squirrels, unlike other species, are active at night. When searching for food or avoiding a predator, they swoop from high in one tree to low on the trunk of another. The larger species, such as the Giant flying squirrel, can glide 100m or more.

◄A female Belding's ground squirrel stands erect and calls to warn her neighbours of an approaching coyote.

A WINTER'S TAIL

The squirrel's tail has many uses, depending on the species. In flying squirrels and tree squirrels it acts as a rudder when leaping, and as a counterweight when balancing on a branch. It may also be used as a signal, informing other squirrels of anger, acceptance or readiness to mate. Species living in hot places fluff out their tails over their backs, to act as a sun-shade. In winter, many tree squirrels sleep in their nests with their tails wrapped around them for warmth.

Grey, red and other tree squirrels do not hibernate. They may stay inside their stick-and-twig nests, called dreys, for several days during bad weather. But they emerge on fine winter days to feed and drink. However, many ground squirrels and marmots hibernate for about 6 months, when their body temperature falls to only a few degrees above freezing.

The woodchuck or groundhog, a marmot of North America, is a famous

▼Young ground squirrels (called "pups") leaving their burrow for the first time. These pups are about 27 days old.

▲ **Types of tree squirrel** An African pygmy squirrel (1) carries a nut. An Abert or Tassel-eared squirrel (*Sciurus aberti*) (2) holds food in its forepaws. An Indian giant squirrel (*Ratufa indica*) (3) leaps to a nearby branch. An American red squirrel (*Tamiasciurus hudsonicus*) (4) hangs by its hind claws while cracking a nut. A Southern flying squirrel (*Glaucomys volans*) (5) glides from its tree hole. Prevost's squirrel (*Callosciurus prevosti*) (6) keeps watch from a sawn-off branch.

hibernator. Legend says that it wakes on February 2nd each year – Groundhog Day. If it sees its shadow, this means sunny cold weather, and it returns to its burrow for another 6 weeks. (This story is unfounded.) When it emerges in spring, it is very thin and has lost up to half its weight.

MAKING A LARDER

Squirrels are famous storers of nuts, seeds and other food to last them through the winter. The Siberian chipmunk may store up to 6kg of food, perhaps 100 times its body weight, in its burrow. This is its source of food when the chipmunk wakes in spring, before new plant growth becomes abundant.

Tree squirrels bury food or hide it in undergrowth, to dig up in winter. European red squirrels can smell pine cones they have buried 30cm below the surface. Grey squirrels may carry acorns 30m from an oak tree before hiding them in a hole. But many squirrels forget where they have buried food, so their activities help to spread seeds and to plant them for future growth.

BREEDING AND SOCIAL LIFE

Most squirrels, like other rodents, are able to breed within a year of being born. There is usually one litter per year. Newborn young are blind and helpless but develop fast, and within 2 months they are ready to leave their nest and fend for themselves.

Most tree squirrels live alone. Each has a territory and chases away intruders. The territory of a male may overlap those of several females. During spring, boundaries break down, and animals come together for a few days to mate.

Ground squirrels tend to be more social and live in groups. Fifty or more Alpine marmots may occupy a large burrow system, with males, females

1

2

▲ **Types of ground squirrel** A Siberian chipmunk with cheek pouches full of food **(1)**. An Alpine marmot stands upright and gives an alarm whistle as it spots a wolf **(2)**. A Shrew-faced ground squirrel, also called the Long-nosed squirrel, extracts termites from a hole in a fallen branch **(3)**. A Western ground squirrel (*Xerus erythropus*) indicates worry by arching and fluffing its tail **(4)**.

◄ The female Belding's ground squirrel carries up to 50 loads of dry grass to line her nest before giving birth.

▶ Black-tailed prairie dogs relax in the Sun. The mound around their tunnel entrance helps to prevent the tunnel flooding.

and young living as one large family. Prairie dogs form even bigger colonies, called "townships", of perhaps 5,000 animals. Each township consists of several family burrows called "coteries". In summer, prairie dogs from different coteries are friendly to each other. In winter, when food is scarcer, coterie members defend their burrows and territories.

SQUIRREL DAMAGE

Two species of squirrel are officially listed as being endangered. But squirrels in general are common, and some species are regarded as pests in certain areas. Prairie dogs used to cause great damage to crops and destroy grassland grazed by farm animals. Poisoning has now made some of them scarce except in remote areas and national parks. The Grey squirrel, in particular, is unloved by foresters, because it strips bark from young trees, probably to eat the sweet-tasting sapwood – but also killing the tree in the process. Guns and traps may reduce its numbers for a time, but there seems to be no permanent answer.

RATS

On a Pacific island a Galapagos rice rat clambers through a bush in search of food. Its long whiskers quiver, and its keen eyes and ears strain to detect danger. Hearing the movements of another animal, lower in the bushes, the rice rat cautiously investigates. It is another rat, but bigger, browner and bolder – a Norway rat. Out of nowhere, a cat pounces. The Norway rat, fast and fierce, gets away. The Galapagos rice rat is less lucky.

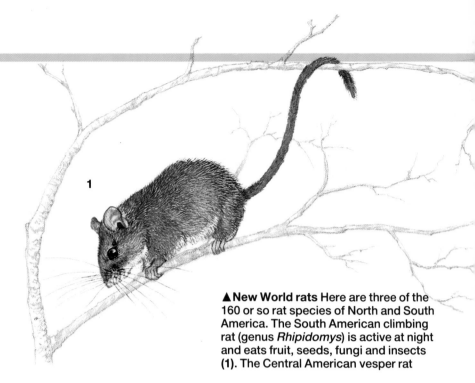

▲ **New World rats** Here are three of the 160 or so rat species of North and South America. The South American climbing rat (genus *Rhipidomys*) is active at night and eats fruit, seeds, fungi and insects (1). The Central American vesper rat

What is the difference between a rat and a mouse? It is mainly size. Most rats – but not all – are larger than most mice. There are no important biological differences. Whether a species is called a rat or a mouse depends partly on local names and traditions. Rats and mice all belong to the same rodent family, Muridae, along with voles, lemmings, hamsters and gerbils. Altogether this family contains 1,082 species, in 241 genera, which is one-quarter of all mammals.

FOUND WORLD-WIDE

Rats live all over the world except in such cold climates as exist in the far north and on especially high mountains. A few species are very familiar and widespread since they live alongside people, in or near buildings, rubbish tips and anywhere else there might be shelter and scraps of food. These include the Norway rat (also called the Brown, Common or Sewer rat) and the Roof rat (also called the Black or Ship rat).

Hundreds of other species of rat live away from people, in rocky mountains, deserts, woodland, grassland and tropical forest. A few are so rare that they are known only from museum specimens or one or two individuals caught in the wild. At least two species of rice rat, from the Caribbean islands, have become extinct. Many other rice rats are threatened – by other rat species brought by people, as well as by cats, dogs and other animals.

RATS Muridae (*450-500 species*)

● ■ 𝓍

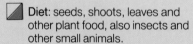 **Habitat:** any land habitat except high mountains, including deserts, steppe, woodland and tropical forest.

Diet: seeds, shoots, leaves and other plant food, also insects and other small animals.

Breeding: litters of 3-7 after pregnancy of 20-50 days; in suitable conditions litters may be every 3-4 weeks.

Size: smallest: mouse-sized (see page 30); largest (Cuming's slender-tailed cloud rat): head-body 48cm, tail 32cm, weight 2kg.

Colour: varies from cream or pale fawn through red, brown and grey to black; ears, nose, feet and tail usually pink-grey; some species have striped backs.

Lifespan: from only a few months up to 2-3 years in bigger species.

Species mentioned in text:
African swamp rats (genus *Otomys*)
Australian water rat (*Hydromys chrysogaster*)
Cuming's slender-tailed cloud rat (*Phloeomys cumingi*)
Galapagos rice rat (genus *Nesoryzomys*)
Giant blind mole-rat (genus *Spalax*)
Lesser bandicoot rat (*Bandicota bengalensis*)
Muller's rat (*Rattus muelleri*)
Multimammate rat (*Praomys natalensis*)
North American woodrat (*Neotoma micropus*)
Norway rat (*Rattus norvegicus*)
Polynesian rat (*R. exulans*)
Roof rat (*R. rattus*)
Zokor (genus *Myospalax*)

(*Nyctomys sumichrasti*), also nocturnal, eats fruit and is completely at home in trees, even nesting there **(2)**. The Central American climbing rat (genus *Tylomys*), another nocturnal rat, prefers trees along river banks and lake shores **(3)**.

THE TYPICAL RAT

The Norway rat is a typical rat. It has a body up to 25cm long, coarse browny-grey fur, a long snout, beady eyes, smallish pinky ears with fine hairs, and strong legs with stout claws. Its tail is furless, up to 20cm long.

Rats, like mice, have four sharp front teeth called incisors, two in the upper jaw and two in the lower. They also have 12 crushing cheek teeth, three on each side of the upper jaw and three on each side of the lower.

While this rodent-like design evolved originally for eating seeds and other plant food, many rats eat whatever they find. The Norway rat takes almost anything, plant or animal, living, dying, dead or rotting. Such a varied diet is one reason why this species is so widespread and numerous.

Another reason for the Norway rat's success is its breeding rate. As with many other species of rat (and mouse), when food and shelter are plentiful a female can have several litters each year. She lives in a burrow and makes a nursery nest of grass, straw, bits of wood and paper, rags and other material. On average, the Norway rat has about 7 young in each litter, but some litters number 10 or more. So one female can raise more than 50 young in a "good" year. However, as many as 50 per cent of these will die from predation or lack of food before they reach breeding age (about 12 weeks). And 95 per cent of adults do not live for more than a year.

The Norway rat came originally from the Caspian Sea area. It began to spread west in the 11th century, and by the early 18th century had reached Britain. It swims well. In the water it is often mistaken for a water vole.

◄The North American woodrat collects sticks and piles them by its nest, in a rocky crack or burrow.

ANOTHER SEAFARING RAT

Another international rodent is the Roof or Black rat. It is not always black – some individuals are brown, grey or even dirty cream. It has a smaller body, larger ears and a longer tail (greater than its body length) than the Norway rat.

The Roof rat came originally from India. Like the Norway rat, it travelled on ships and in cargoes, reaching western Europe in the 11th century. Being a tropical creature by nature, it tended to stay near warm and sheltered places. When the bigger, bolder Norway rat arrived, the Black rat became less common.

Today, both species live in many countries across the world. The Roof rat tends to be more common in tropical regions, infesting towns and villages. The Norway rat is more numerous in temperate areas and in cities and ports in the tropics.

RATS OF TWO WORLDS

The Norway and Roof rats belong to the group known as Old World rats and mice (Murinae). There are 406 species, of which about 200-250 are regarded as rats. They inhabit all of Europe, Africa, central and southern Asia and Australia. Some species live mainly in burrows, others spend almost all their lives in trees. All are chiefly herbivores, eating seeds, shoots, fruits and leaves.

There are more rat species in the warmer and damper regions of Africa and Asia than there are in Europe or in dry or cold areas. There are also many species in the islands of South-east Asia. In the Philippines alone there are 30 rat species found nowhere else. They include Cuming's slender-tailed cloud rat (the largest rat species) and two other large species. In New Guinea there are another six sizeable species.

For the past 30 million years, the New World rats and mice (Hesperomyinae) have evolved separately from

their Old World cousins. There are now 366 species, of which about 160 are commonly called rats. Like their counterparts in the Old World, they live a variety of life-styles.

The Old and New World rats also show a similar range of adaptations. In climbing species the tail has become a long balancing or a grasping organ. The big toes of hands and feet of tree-living species are often opposable, allowing the animals to grasp thin branches.

OTHER RAT GROUPS

Related to the Old and New World rats are about eight other groups of rats. The African swamp or vlei rats live in central and southern Africa, especially in upland areas. They have blunt noses, long fur and short tails, and look more like voles than typical rats. They prefer damp places and eat grass and other tough-stemmed plants.

In South-east Asia and Australia there are about 20 species of Austra-

lian water rats that are well suited to life in marshes and rivers. The largest is the Australian water rat itself, which may weigh more than 1kg. It has webbed hind feet and hunts underwater by day for fish, frogs, crabs, insects and shellfish. It is often mistaken for a platypus.

The zokors are burrowing, vole-like rats found in dry grassland and woods in central Asia and China. They have small eyes and ears and very large front claws for digging. They eat roots and bulbs, sometimes surfacing to forage for seeds. Zokors collect huge underground stores of food for the winter.

UNDERGROUND RATS

Perhaps the oddest rats are the blind mole-rats of Africa, the Middle East and Western Asia. The largest is the

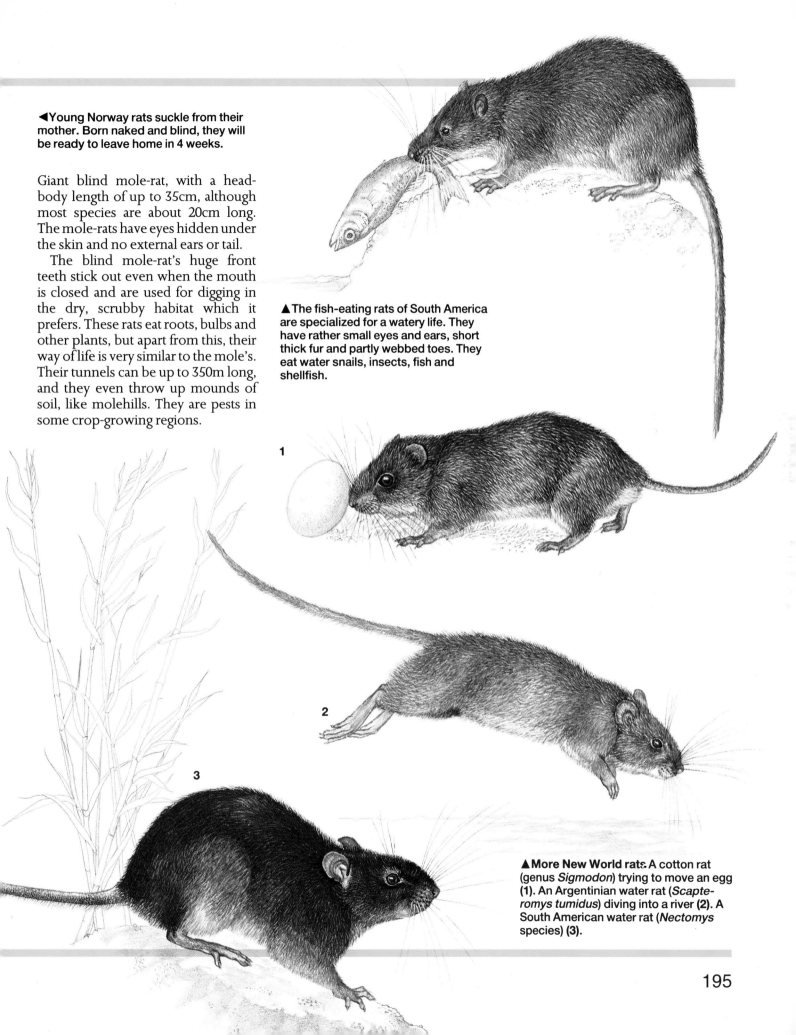

◀Young Norway rats suckle from their mother. Born naked and blind, they will be ready to leave home in 4 weeks.

Giant blind mole-rat, with a head-body length of up to 35cm, although most species are about 20cm long. The mole-rats have eyes hidden under the skin and no external ears or tail.

The blind mole-rat's huge front teeth stick out even when the mouth is closed and are used for digging in the dry, scrubby habitat which it prefers. These rats eat roots, bulbs and other plants, but apart from this, their way of life is very similar to the mole's. Their tunnels can be up to 350m long, and they even throw up mounds of soil, like molehills. They are pests in some crop-growing regions.

▲The fish-eating rats of South America are specialized for a watery life. They have rather small eyes and ears, short thick fur and partly webbed toes. They eat water snails, insects, fish and shellfish.

▲More New World rats. A cotton rat (genus *Sigmodon*) trying to move an egg (1). An Argentinian water rat (*Scapteromys tumidus*) diving into a river (2). A South American water rat (*Nectomys* species) (3).

PESTS AND DISEASES

Most species of rat are rarely seen by people, but a few are pests. Besides the Norway rat and Roof rat, they include the Multimammate rat in Africa, the Polynesian rat in Asia and the Lesser bandicoot rat in India.

All these rats, with their sharp, ever-growing incisors, chew away water-pipes and drains, making them leak, and gnash through electricity cables, causing power cuts. They gnaw their way into food stores (especially grain), eating what they can and contaminating the food with their urine and droppings. Their burrowing undermines walls and foundations – buildings have collapsed due to warrens of rat tunnels beneath.

Rats also carry disease. In the 14th century millions of Europeans died from bubonic plague, the Black Death. The bacteria (germs) causing the plague were carried by Roof rats. Fleas sucked blood from the rats, took in the bacteria and then bit people, passing on the disease. A number of serious diseases, including lassa fever, rat-bite fever, Weil's disease (leptospirosis) and a form of typhus, are today spread by the bite, urine, droppings and parasites of rats.

Pest rat species have been hunted, poisoned and trapped over the centuries. Millions have been killed. Yet they are adaptable and agile, able to eat almost anything and breed very quickly. Many species have now acquired resistance to conventional rodent poisons, such as warfarin. In the sewers and underground tunnels of most large cities, the rat population continues to increase. It is unlikely we will ever be able to banish them completely from areas where people live and work.

▶A Muller's rat of warm damp regions of the Far East shows the typical rat's agility as it grasps with its sharp claws and balances using its tail.

MICE

On a wheat farm in southern Canada labourers arriving for work one morning find that most of the season's harvest has been destroyed overnight by mice. The mice have chewed and broken their way into the sacks of grain, and either eaten the contents or contaminated it with their urine and droppings. The farmer calls in the pest control department, which taints the rest of the grain with poison. Within two days, several thousand mice are killed. The only problem that remains is to remove the poisoned mice before other animals eat them.

A mouse is a small rat – or, to put it the other way round, a rat is a large mouse. There is no real biological difference between mice and rats. Scientists include them all in the same family (Muridae). Of the 1,082 species in this family, between 350 and 400 are commonly called mice. They live all over the world except on high mountains, and in lakes and oceans.

Most experts agree that the House mouse, which has followed people to every continent, is the world's most numerous mammal. The Australian farmer who found 28,000 House mice dead on his veranda, after putting down poison overnight, would probably agree.

BUNDLE OF ENERGY

The Wood mouse of Europe and Asia is a typical mouse. It has a head and body about 9cm long, and a finely haired, scaly-looking tail of about the same length. Its big, black, beady eyes and large fine-haired ears indicate that it is active by night. It also has a keen

◀The mole mice of South America live in underground burrows and eat mainly termites and other insects.

▲The American harvest mouse, like its Old World cousin, builds ball-shaped grass nests near the ground.

sense of smell and many large, sensitive whiskers on its snout. The fur is generally chestnut or sandy-brown on the back and much lighter, even white, on the underparts, with a small yellow streak on the chest.

The Wood mouse is a very active animal, scrabbling and bounding about as it forages over its territory. Like most mice, it lives alone. It sniffs new objects cautiously and is always looking and listening for predators. Even so, Wood mice are commonly caught by foxes, cats and owls.

MICE Muridae (*400 species*)

● ▣ ☠

■ **Habitat:** any land habitat except high mountains, including deserts, steppe, woodland and tropical forest.

■ **Diet:** seeds and other plant food, also some animal food; a few

species completely insectivorous.

◯ **Breeding:** usually 1-3 litters per year; litters of 2-5 after pregnancy of 3-4 weeks; in suitable conditions litters monthly in some species.

Size: smallest (pygmy mice): head-body 4.5cm, tail 3cm, weight 6g; largest the size of a small rat.

Colour: cream or pale fawn through red, brown and grey to almost black, often with paler underparts; tail may be naked or furry; some species have striped backs.

Lifespan: from a few months to 2 years.

Species mentioned in text:
American harvest mouse (*Reithrodontomys humilis*)

Climbing wood mouse (*Praomys alleni*)
Deer mice (*Peromyscus* species)
Fawn hopping mouse (*Notomys cervinus*)
Grasshopper mice (*Onychomys* species)
Harvest mouse (*Micromys minutus*)
House mouse (*Mus musculus*)
Larger pygmy mouse (*M. triton*)
Leaf-eared mice (*Phyllotis* species)
Mole mice (*Notiomys* species)
New World pygmy mice (*Baiomys* species)
Peter's striped mouse (*Hybomys univittatus*)
Pygmy mouse (*Mus minutoides*)
Shrew mouse (*Blarinomys breviceps*)
Volcano mouse (*Neotomodon alstoni*)
Water mice (*Rheomys* species)
Wood or Long-tailed field mouse (*Apodemus sylvaticus*)
Yellow-necked field mouse (*A. flavicollis*)

BREEDING LIKE MICE

Despite its name, the Wood mouse is found in a variety of habitats, including woodland, scrubland, hedge, moor, mountain and sand dunes, and in gardens and around outbuildings. It is often mistaken for the House mouse, although it does not have the strong smell of the House mouse.

The Wood mouse digs a burrow and hides in it by day, emerging to feed at night. It feeds mainly on buds and seeds, including nuts, which it is expert at opening with its incisor teeth. It stores food in the burrow, and the female gives birth there, in a nest lined with grass and moss. She may have four or five litters each year through the spring and summer, with about five young in each. So numbers can build up quickly, and this species is sometimes a pest around farms and where food is stored.

►The Harvest mouse's nest, about 7cm across, is woven usually on grass stems or sometimes into a thorn bush.

▼A Yellow-necked field mouse scurries past rose hips by moonlight, carrying a hazel nut in its sharp front teeth.

LIFE IN TALL GRASS

Another European species is the Harvest mouse. This is one of the smallest rodents, with a body weight of only 7g when fully grown. It lives in fields of crops and tall grass along hedges, motorways and railway and canal embankments.

The Harvest mouse is famous for its tennis-ball-sized nests, which it weaves from living, shredded grass leaves and stems. It rests in such a nest, or in a burrow or hedgerow, between bouts of great activity – 3 hours sleeping and 3 hours feeding. This means the Harvest mouse is active by day and so it often falls prey to hawks, weasels, snakes and other hunters.

Young Harvest mice are born in a special nursery nest, more strongly built than the usual resting nest, between 10cm and 30cm from the ground. After a pregnancy of 21 days the female gives birth to between 5 and 8 young (rarely 12 or more). Their eyes open at 8 days, they begin to leave the nest after 12 days, and they are frequently independent of their mother at 15 days.

OLD WORLD MICE

The mice species mentioned so far are only some of the 150 to 200 species of Old World mice that live in Europe,

▲Newborn mice are hairless and cannot see or hear. But within 3 weeks they will be able to fend for themselves.

▶New World mice A Pygmy mouse from southern North America (1); Deer mouse from central North America (2); Leaf-eared mouse from central South America (3).

▼Leaf-eared mice, unlike most mice, are active by day. They often bask on sunny rocks, listening intently.

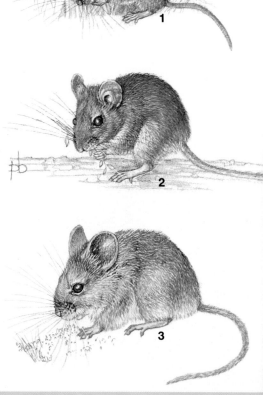

Africa, Asia and Australia. They belong to the Murinae group.

Many mice live in tropical forests. One research project in Uganda found four species of mice (as well as seven rat species) living together in one small area. The Pygmy mouse stayed on the ground and ate a variety of plants and small animals. So did the Larger pygmy mouse, although it tended to take larger food items. The Climbing wood mouse lived among the branches of low bushes, seldom coming to the ground or going higher than about 60cm. Peter's striped mouse lived in taller branches and ate plant food. Living at different levels and taking different types of food, these mice were able to exist together.

MICE OF THE AMERICAS
About 200 mice species belong to the New World mice and rats (Hesperomyinae). Among the most familiar are the deer or white-footed mice of North and Central America. The various species of deer mice live on the ground and in trees, in all types of habitat from deserts to rocky hills and woodland. Their way of life is similar to that of the Old World mice.

The Volcano mouse is a close relative of the deer mice. It lives on the steep volcanic slopes of central Mexico, at heights of up to 4,300m, and hides in burrows and crevices in and among the rocks.

Some of the most unusual mice are the water mice of Central America. They live in mountain streams and feed on water snails and fish. Large-bodied for mice, with a head-body length of up to 19cm, they have webbed hind feet with bristly hairs on the outside, to aid swimming.

►Grasshopper mice, which range from southern Canada to central Mexico, give a shrill squeak when they see one another. This may help to keep them evenly spaced.

Also in South America live the burrowing and mole mice. These have large front claws, up to 7mm long, for efficient digging. One species, the Shrew mouse, has tiny eyes, and its ears are hidden in its thick fur. It spends its life burrowing in the forest floor, eating mainly insects and other small creatures.

CLIMBING AND BURROWING
Apart from the two major groups, Old World and New World mice, there are also other, smaller groups of mice. One of these is the African climbing mice (Dendromurinae), which live mainly in grassland areas of Central and Southern Africa. New species of these animals are discovered every few years, and among them are some very distinctive mice.

The climbing mice themselves are agile, with long tails and slender feet. Their way of life is rather like that of the Harvest mouse, and some species build ball-shaped nests of grass. They feed on seeds, fruits and small animals such as beetles, lizards and birds.

Also in this group are the fat mice, which make large burrows. Before the dry season they feed eagerly and put on thick layers of body fat. During the dry season they stay in their burrows, in a form of hibernation. They also do this during the day in the wet season. Mice are generally such busy creatures, but the fat mice are inactive in the extreme.

OF MICE AND MEN
Most species of mice have a high breeding rate. It is one of their survival methods, since they are small and relatively defenceless animals. Another means of survival is their wide choice of food. For example, Harvest mice eat seeds, fruits, buds, shoots and some insects such as small beetles. Wood mice also have a varied diet, feeding on seeds and other plant food, worms, grubs and snails – after nibbling through the shells.

House mice are even less fussy and make meals of lard, butter, soap, candle wax, frozen foods such as meat and vegetables, paper, cardboard, leather and much else besides. This is one reason why they are so numerous and widespread. Other reasons are that in many parts of the world they have become resistant to normal rodent poisons and, if disturbed, they will readily leave one home and establish another without stress.

Besides being pests, mice have also given benefit to people. They have long been kept as pets, and more than 3,000 years ago "mouse worship" was practised in Western Asia. Today strains of mice with white, black and patched fur, bred originally from the House mouse, are used in laboratory experiments for testing new medicines and chemicals. This small rodent is one of the most useful, as well as one of the most destructive, creatures on Earth.

▼The 49 species of deer mice are widespread across North America. They eat seeds and are active at night.

► The House mouse has lived alongside people for thousands of years, perhaps since the first farmers of the Middle East cultivated and stored grain.

▼ **Old World mice** A Harsh-furred mouse (*Lophuromys sikapusi*) from Africa eats an insect (**1**). Spiny mice (*Acomys* species) have strong, spiky hairs on their backs (**2**). The Pencil-tailed tree mouse (*Chiropodomys gliroides*) has broad feet for a good grip and a long, tufted tail for balance (**3**). The Fawn hopping mouse of Australia has whiskers that measure more than half its body length (**4**). A Four-striped grass mouse (*Rhabdomys pumilio*) shows its camouflaging stripes while cleaning (**5**).

VOLES AND LEMMINGS

In late summer a Norway lemming noses its way down a bank. It is leaving to find new pasture. The grasslands here have become too crowded with others of its kind. More and more lemmings join the procession, all migrating from over-populated homelands. As they march they are funnelled into a strip of land sticking into a lake. Lemmings can swim, and they plunge in, hoping for fresh grass on the far side. But the lake is too wide, and they all drown.

▼A Bank vole nibbles an acorn held by its forefeet. This species lives in wood, scrub and marsh as well as hedgebanks.

VOLES AND LEMMINGS Muridae; sub-family: Microtinae (*110 species*)

Habitat: tundra, scrub, open forest, grassland, rocky areas.

Diet: plants; a few species eat small insects and molluscs.

Breeding: average 3 litters per year, litters of 3-7.

Size: small voles: head-body 8cm, tail 3cm, weight 17g; largest (muskrat): head-body 36cm, tail 28cm, weight 1.4kg.

Colour: fawn, brown and grey to almost black.

Lifespan: a few months to 2 years.

Species mentioned in text:
Bank vole (*Clethrionomys glareolus*)
Collared or Arctic lemming (*Dicrostonyx torquatus*)
European water vole (*Arvicola terrestris*)
Muskrat (*Ondata zibethicus*)
Norway lemming (*Lemmus lemmus*)
Prairie vole (*Microtus ochrogaster*)

Voles and lemmings are small, dumpy rodents. They have thick fur, short legs, blunt noses, small eyes and ears, and tails usually less than half the length of the body. They have many similarities with their cousins, the mice and rats. They too are mainly plant-eaters. They can breed at a great rate when conditions are good. And they live in all types of habitat.

NORTHERN HOMES

However, unlike mice and rats, voles and lemmings live only in the Northern hemisphere. They do not inhabit tropical areas, nor are they nocturnal. Most species are active in bursts through the day and night, with brief rest periods between. This makes

▲ The European water vole is at home in streams and lakes. Here one searches a river bank for food.

◄Norway lemmings, like other lemmings and voles, usually live alone. When two individuals meet, they may be aggressive and defend their territories. Here two males box (1), wrestle (2) and threaten(3).

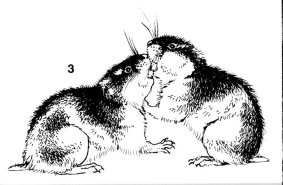

▼During a mass migration, many lemmings die. This is not intentional suicide, but accidental drowning.

them vulnerable to a host of daytime and nocturnal predators, such as weasels, stoats, foxes, snakes, cats, owls, skuas and ravens.

Lemmings live in areas of coniferous forest, moor and the treeless, bleak tundra of the far north. Some vole species are found here too, but most live farther south, in temperate woodland, scrub and grassland. The mole-voles of central Asia are specialized for a burrowing life, with no visible ears and a cylindrical body. Their front teeth stick out forwards and are used for digging.

LONERS AND COLONIES

Most voles and lemmings live alone. They mark their territories using body secretions, and the odours warn others to keep out. Each animal defends its territory, especially at breeding time, by behaving aggressively, calling and even fighting intruders if necessary.

A few species, such as some meadow voles of North America, live in colonies. They dig complicated tunnels and keep in touch using a variety of squeaks, whistles and chirrups.

As with most rodents, young voles and lemmings are born blind and

205

helpless. The female usually gives birth in a nest of dry grass, lichen or other vegetation, in a burrow. The average number in a litter varies from 2 to 12, depending on species, food supply and other conditions.

Parental care is the work of the mother, who guards her young carefully. If they wander from the nest, she finds them by their squeaks and brings them back. Only in the Prairie vole does the male help, grooming the young and keeping the runways and burrows clean.

TUNNELS UNDER THE SNOW
Lemmings are the most numerous small mammals in the tundra. During the short summer they feed on grasses, herbs and other plants that grow in the swampy soil. During the long, cold winter, they remain active by digging tunnels at ground level under the snow and feeding on roots, shoots, mosses, lichens and other plant matter. The blanket of snow is a good insulator. Bitter winds above may lower the air temperature to minus 40°C, but in the snow burrows it rarely falls much below freezing.

Norway lemmings live in the tundra of Scandinavia and Siberia. In winter they stay under the snow, tunnelling, feeding and breeding in snug underground nests. With the spring thaw, these lemmings avoid floods by moving to higher ground or to more wooded areas. Here they make shallow tunnels in the soil, travel by well-marked runways through the undergrowth, and continue to feed and breed.

POPULATION EXPLOSION
The ability of the Norway lemming (and many other lemming species) to breed almost all year round means that its numbers can increase dramatically. Females mate before they are a month old, males soon after. With room to establish a territory and plentiful food, a female can have one

▲A Collared lemming cares for her young in their grassy nest on the edge of the treeless Arctic tundra.

litter each month. There is an average of six young per litter.

In some years, the Norway lemming population increases very quickly. It may rise from less than 5 animals per hectare (about the area of two soccer pitches) to more than 300 animals. This happens roughly every 3 or 4 years.

The result is overcrowding, with not enough food to go around and too many encounters between individuals as each forages over its shrinking territory. Gradually some of the extra lemmings are forced to seek better conditions. This is the famous "lemming migration".

ON THE MARCH
Many tales surround the mass marches of lemmings. They happen in several species, not only in the Norway lemming. Thousands of animals descend from uplands and woods into the lowland fields, destroying crops and polluting rivers and wells with their dead bodies.

8

7

◀Types of vole and lemming A muskrat sits on its house of branches and twigs (1). A tree-living species, the Red-tree vole (*Phenacomys longicaudatus*) (2). A Norway lemming sniffs the air (3). A Collared lemming in its white winter coat(4), and in its brown summer fur (5). A Taiga vole (*Microtus xanothognathus*) on its hind legs keeps watch (6). A Meadow vole (*Microtus pennsylvanicus*) drums an alarm signal with its hind foot (7). A Southern mole-vole (*Ellobius fuscocapillus*) (8).

But these great marches are not deliberate suicide – despite what people once believed. Barriers such as mountains and rivers cause the travelling lemmings gradually to collect in enormous groups. When they reach the shore of a lake or the sea, the only answer is to try to swim across. Normally, lemmings are reasonable swimmers and attempt only short trips in the water. But on migration they seem to get caught in mass panic, unable to use normal judgement. They set off to swim across a sea or clamber down a vertical cliff. As a result, they die in their efforts to find new, unoccupied lands.

Lemming population explosions affect other animals. Arctic foxes, one of their chief predators, also become more numerous as the lemmings increase and the foxes have more food. Trappers in the fur trade realized that in some years they caught few foxes, then 3 or 4 years later the numbers would be very high, only to fall suddenly once again. Records of the Hudson Bay Company from 1870 to 1920 show fox pelt numbers varying from 200 to 6,000 in such a cycle.

207

WATERY LIFE

The muskrat is a very large vole, specialized for an aquatic life. Its name comes from the strong smell of the secretions made in two glands at the base of its tail. The muskrat's hind feet are partly webbed and have a fringe of stiff hairs, to aid swimming. Its tail is almost hairless, scaly and flattened from side to side – it works as a rudder in the water. The outer protective fur is coarse and long, varying in colour from grey-brown to black. The under-fur is short, thick and very tough. It is sold by traders as the valuable "musquash", which is the name given to the animal by the Canadian Plains Indians.

Muskrats live in North America, in swamps, rivers and lakes. They eat water plants and also some animals such as mussels, crayfish, snails and fish. They build nests in grassy banks and dig elaborate tunnels with entrances that are often under water.

These voles were taken to Europe, to breed on fur farms. They escaped and now live wild in certain areas, such as the Netherlands. They can do great damage, tunnelling into dykes and dams and eating crops. In temperate climates they can breed from spring to autumn and raise several families each year, and so quickly become pests.

Also, in Europe, in the absence of many of their natural predators – coyotes, raccoons, turtles, water snakes and alligators – muskrats can spread far and wide. However, in other places in the world they have been released on purpose, since their feeding prevents waterways from becoming choked by weeds.

◄The European water vole's glossy brown outer coat hides the short, dense underfur that keeps the animal warm and dry.

HAMSTERS

As spring warms the frozen ground of the Russian steppes, hamsters awaken from their winter hibernation and emerge in search of food. Because food is often scarce, they must search a wide area. Each hamster jealously guards its own territory. Two hamsters meet along the edge of their territories and begin to fight one another. One of them receives deep wounds and runs away. These fierce little creatures will attack animals ten times their own size.

▲ The Common hamster's cheek pouches consist of loose folds of skin. The pouches expand as food is pushed in.

Hamsters are rodents related to rats and mice. The familiar Golden hamster, often kept as a pet, has a squat, rounded body, blunt face, large ears and a tiny tail. Other hamsters are more mouse-like, with a pointed snout and a longer tail.

Hamsters are solitary animals, and each one digs its own underground burrow about 1m below the surface. The Common hamster builds a warren with several entrances and many chambers. One chamber may be used for sleeping, a second as a lavatory and others as food stores.

FOOD HOARDS

The hamsters' diet consists mainly of plant material, including roots, seeds and leaves, but they also eat insects and the occasional snake or young bird. They carry food in their cheek pouches. The front paws are used like hands to pack seeds and nuts into these elastic folds of skin. When food is plentiful, hamsters gather it into their cheek pouches and in this way

◄ The dwarf Dzungarian hamster is not much bigger than a fir cone.

carry it underground to their burrows. Stored there, it lasts throughout the barren winter months. The storage chamber of a single Common hamster was found to contain 90kg of food.

FAST BREEDING

When they are kept in artificially warm conditions in cages, Golden hamsters produce young at any time of the year. In the wild they normally breed just twice, in spring and summer. Mating adults make high-pitched squeaks which cannot be picked up by the human ear. Two weeks after mating, the blind naked young are born in a nest lined with soft wool and grasses. The male plays no part in raising his offspring. The female suckles them for about 3 weeks.

The young are able to mate at the age of about 2 or 3 months. Common hamsters mature even earlier, at about 6 weeks. Given plenty of food, they have been known to breed even before they leave the nest.

Individual hamsters only live for 2 or 3 years in the wild, but because they reproduce quickly their numbers remain high. All of the millions of Golden hamsters in Western Europe and North America have been bred from a group of 13 originally collected in Syria in 1930.

HAMSTERS Muridae (24 species)

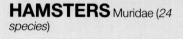

● ◼

▲ Habitat: dry steppe, mountains, cultivated land.

◪ Diet: plant material, sometimes insects.

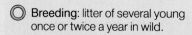

◯ Breeding: litter of several young once or twice a year in wild.

Size: head-body 5.3-10.2cm, weight 50g (Dzungarian hamster); head-body 20-28cm, weight 900g (Common hamster).

Colour: grey to tawny with white patches.

Lifespan: 2-3 years in wild.

Species mentioned in text:
Common or Black-bellied hamster
    (*Cricetus cricetus*)
Dzungarian hamster (*Phodopus sungorus*)
Golden hamster (*Mesocricetus auratus*)
Korean grey rat (*Cricetulus triton*)

▲The Common hamster has large mobile ears for picking up the smallest sounds. The front paws are used like hands for holding food.

ENEMIES AND PREDATORS

In many places hamsters are treated as pests because they damage crops. They are particularly partial to wheat, barley, millet, soy beans, peas, potatoes, carrots and beets. They are also trapped for their skins and for food. Happily, they mainly occur in cold, barren places where people do not live. Their main enemies are wolves and polecats, which can dig them out of burrows with their powerful claws.

The Korean grey rat, which is a hamster despite its name, rolls over on to its back and shrieks if attacked. This shock tactic may give it just enough time to escape from a very surprised predator.

GERBILS

Quietly and cautiously, a gerbil peeps out of its burrow. It is dusk on the dry Asian grassland, and cool enough to begin the nightly search for food. This small, mouse-like rodent begins to creep along a bank, beady-eyed and whiskers quivering, sniffing out seeds.

Many people recognize the gerbil (or jerbil as it is sometimes spelt), since it is often kept as a pet. But there is not just one species of gerbil – there are about 80. They live in Africa, the Middle East and across central Asia to India and China. The familiar pet is usually a Mongolian gerbil.

Gerbils are cousins of rats and mice, which they resemble except for their furry tails. Some species are called rats or sand rats, and others are called jirds or dipodils, but they all belong to the gerbil group.

Gerbils are specialized for life in dry places such as desert, dry savannah, steppe grassland and rocky areas. Those from very dry places usually live alone. In scrub or grassland, where food is more plentiful, they may live in pairs or groups of up to 20.

To avoid the heat and being seen by predators, gerbils usually hide by day in their burrows. These are about 50cm deep, and the air in them is cool and moist all the time. To keep the burrow cool, some gerbils block its entrance with stones or bits of plants. At night, when it is not so hot, they emerge under cover of darkness for a night-time feast.

SEEDS AS SPONGES

Gerbils eat mainly seeds and other parts of plants such as roots, shoots, buds, leaves and fruits. But in such harsh surroundings, any food is welcome. Some gerbil species eat insects, lizards, worms and other small creatures, as well as plants. Wagner's gerbil eats snails, leaving big piles of empty shells outside its burrow.

GERBILS Gerbillinae (*81 species*)

● ◪

◓ Habitat: dry places such as desert, scrub, grassland.

◪ Diet: seeds and other plant food; sometimes insects and other small animals.

◯ Breeding: in driest areas 1 litter after rainy season, in damper places up to 3 litters through year, average 3-5 young per litter.

Size: head-body 7-20cm; tail 7-22cm; weight 8-190g.

Colour: pale grey, reddish or brown to almost black; varies within species to match colour of surroundings.

Lifespan: 1-2 years.

Species mentioned in text:
Great gerbil (*Rhombomys opimus*)
Mongolian gerbil (*Meriones unguiculatus*)
South African pygmy gerbil (*Gerbillurus paeba*)
Wagner's gerbil (*Gerbillus dasyurus*)

All animals need water to survive. In the gerbil's dry surroundings, there is little water to drink, and the food is often dry too. The gerbil is an expert at making the best of what is available. When it starts to feed, the dew is falling and the seeds soak up some of this moisture, like tiny sponges. To save more moisture, gerbils produce no more than a few tiny drops of urine each day.

Gerbils often carry food back to the burrow, to eat in safety or store until later. In the damp burrow, the food absorbs yet more moisture. The Great gerbil of central Asia even stores food outside its burrow, in piles more than 1m high!

ATTACKS FROM THE AIR

Many gerbils fall victim to flying predators, such as owls and hawks. But most species are well adapted to reduce the risk of being captured. They are coloured like their surroundings, and have a keen sense of hearing.

▲Like most gerbils, the South African pygmy gerbil is a hoarder. It stores food in its burrow, to eat when times are hard.

◄Busy about their business A South African pygmy gerbil **(1)** cleans its whiskers. A Tamarisk gerbil (*Meriones tamariscinus*) **(2)** looks for danger. A Libyan jird (*Meriones libycus*) **(3)** leaps at an enemy, while a Cape short-eared gerbil (*Desmondillus auricularis*) **(4)** crouches in submission. A Great gerbil **(5)**, one of the largest species, marks its territory with a pile of sand, urine and droppings. The small *Gerbillus gerbillus* **(6)** does the same with fluid from a gland on its underside. A female Mongolian gerbil **(7)** raises her neck-fur during courtship. A Fat sand rat (*Psammomys obesus*) **(8)** sniffs a ball of sand and urine left by a neighbour.

DORMICE

The cold October wind sweeps through a small European town. For several days a dormouse has been making a snug nest of dry grass and moss in a thick hedge bordering a garden. It is a tubby animal, yet it still climbs nimbly through the bushes as it feeds on berries and nuts. Eventually the dormouse settles to sleep in the nest. When it wakes, it will be the middle of spring.

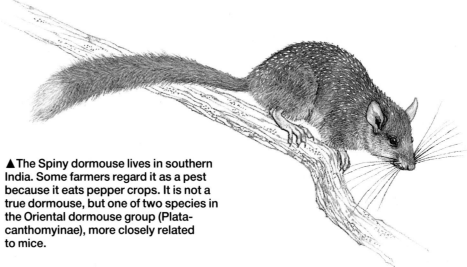

▲The Spiny dormouse lives in southern India. Some farmers regard it as a pest because it eats pepper crops. It is not a true dormouse, but one of two species in the Oriental dormouse group (Platacanthomyinae), more closely related to mice.

The dormouse has nothing to do with doors. Its English name comes from the French word *dormir*, meaning "to sleep". And in Europe this is what a dormouse does. For about 7 months every year it sleeps, non-stop, in deep hibernation through the winter.

During autumn the dormouse feeds greedily on fruits, nuts and berries, building up a layer of body fat. The fat will provide energy for the long winter sleep. As it goes into hibernation, the dormouse's body temperature falls. Its breathing and heartbeat slow down. It will not wake up, even if one prods or pokes it, like the dormouse at the tea-party in *Alice in Wonderland*. Hibernation is one way of surviving the winter, when there is little food, and the freezing temperatures are dangerous for many small animals.

CALLING AND WHISTLING
In about April, warmer weather wakes the dormouse from its slumber. Thin again, it feeds hungrily on buds, shoots, flowers and small creatures. It is now the mating season, and dormice make a variety of noises at this time. The female Garden dormouse whistles to attract her mate. The male Edible dormouse makes a squeaky call as he chases a female.

Edible dormice are so named because the Romans used to keep them in cages and fatten them for food. One of the world's first cookbooks, written by Epicius of Ancient Rome, has a recipe for stuffed dormouse. The Edible dormouse has a very bushy tail and looks like a Grey squirrel. Most other species have rusty red or brown fur and look like a cross between a squirrel and a mouse.

NURSERY NEST
Around 3 to 4 weeks after mating, the female dormouse builds a ball-shaped nest in a tree hole or the crook of a branch. She lines it with feathers and hairs. Here she gives birth to about four blind, furless, helpless young.

▶The Garden dormouse, like its relatives, has sharp, curved claws and is an expert climber.

After 3 weeks the young can see and hear. By 6 weeks they are fending for themselves. They are able to breed when about a year old, towards the end of their first hibernation.

Most species of dormouse live in loose groups and do not stray from their home range. Locally they are quite common. The Garden dormouse has taken advantage of human presence and lives in gardens in towns and villages, although it also inhabits forests and rocky places.

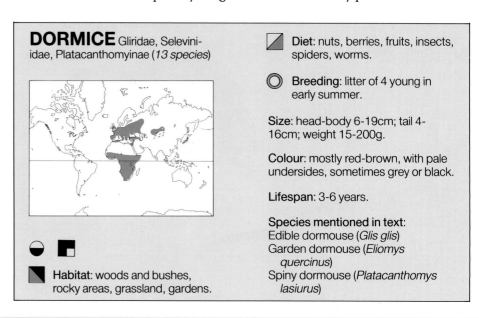

DORMICE Gliridae, Selevini-idae, Platacanthomyinae (*13 species*)

◐ ◧

▨ **Habitat:** woods and bushes, rocky areas, grassland, gardens.

◪ **Diet:** nuts, berries, fruits, insects, spiders, worms.

◎ **Breeding:** litter of 4 young in early summer.

Size: head-body 6-19cm; tail 4-16cm; weight 15-200g.

Colour: mostly red-brown, with pale undersides, sometimes grey or black.

Lifespan: 3-6 years.

Species mentioned in text:
Edible dormouse (*Glis glis*)
Garden dormouse (*Eliomys quercinus*)
Spiny dormouse (*Platacanthomys lasiurus*)

JERBOAS

In the harsh Saharan sunset, the light and heat fade, as three jerboas hop from a burrow and begin the night's foraging. But one starts to stray, feeding on a wind-blown trail of seeds. A desert fox, watching nearby, creeps quietly between this animal and its burrow. The jerboa's large ears detect the faint sound of the fox padding across the sand. With two huge leaps the jerboa tries to escape, but the fox is too quick. All that's left of the jerboa are entrails on a blood-stained patch of sand.

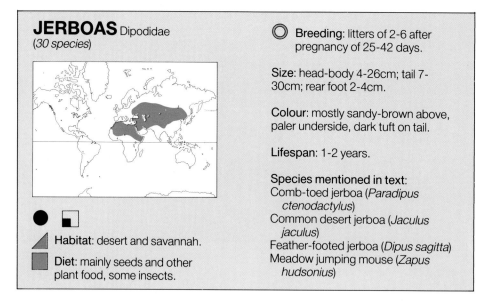

JERBOAS Dipodidae
(*30 species*)

● ■

▲ Habitat: desert and savannah.

■ Diet: mainly seeds and other plant food, some insects.

○ Breeding: litters of 2-6 after pregnancy of 25-42 days.

Size: head-body 4-26cm; tail 7-30cm; rear foot 2-4cm.

Colour: mostly sandy-brown above, paler underside, dark tuft on tail.

Lifespan: 1-2 years.

Species mentioned in text:
Comb-toed jerboa (*Paradipus ctenodactylus*)
Common desert jerboa (*Jaculus jaculus*)
Feather-footed jerboa (*Dipus sagitta*)
Meadow jumping mouse (*Zapus hudsonius*)

▲ A desert jerboa scrabbles in the sand with its short forelegs, looking for seeds, shoots and other tidbits.

▼ A jerboa uses its long tail to balance when leaping, and also as a prop to lean on when standing still. These small rodents hop distances many times their own body size – a desert jerboa can jump 3m with each leap.

The jerboa's body design, with its enormously long hind legs, shows at once that this animal is built for jumping. The hind legs are at least four times longer than the front ones, and the strong rod-like bones act as levers to propel the animal forwards in great bounds.

Jerboas do not leap everywhere, however. When not in a hurry they can hop slowly, or even walk, using only their hind legs.

HAIRY FEET
Species of jerboa living in sandy areas have tufts of fur on the undersides of their feet. These act as "snowshoes", preventing them from sinking into the soft sand, and they also help gain a grip when taking off on a leap. The Feather-footed jerboa of China and Russia and the Comb-toed jerboa of Russia are named after their furry feet.

Hairy feet are useful too when digging for food or making a burrow. The jerboa scrapes away soil using its forelegs and its rodent's large front teeth, and kicks away the soil behind with its powerful hind legs.

HOMES FROM HOME
Most species of jerboa live in hot deserts, sandy scrubland and other dry places, across North Africa and central Asia. Since there are few trees or bushes in which to hide, jerboas dig burrows. Here they stay during the day, away from the heat and the drying effect of the Sun. At night they emerge to search for food such as seeds, leaves and shoots and also beetles and other insects. Their large eyes help them see in the dark, and their big ears detect faint sounds.

The Common desert jerboa lives in loose groups, but most other species

live alone. Each jerboa may have several burrows in the area where it lives. There is usually one main burrow, which is used most of the time, and where a female gives birth to her young. This may be as deep as 2m and have several connecting chambers and passages, plus "larders" for food storage. There is often a spare exit for emergencies, or a chamber that is just under the surface, from where the jerboa can "burst" out of the ground and make its escape.

There are also smaller burrows, from 10 to 50cm long, which the jerboa uses during the day or at night if it cannot return to its main burrow.

In the more northern parts of their range, jerboas also have hibernating burrows. Here they sleep through the cold winter. In spring they mate, and the young are born in a nest deep in the nursery burrow. In about 2 months they are ready to fend for themselves. Jerboas average two litters a year.

Related to the jerboas, and with the same large hind feet for hopping, are the jumping mice (family Zapodidae). There are 14 species, living across central North America, Eastern Europe and central Asia.

▲The Meadow jumping mouse is a relative of the jerboas. It has the same hopping habits, but it does not burrow.

▼A desert jerboa's large ears listen for predators. They also lose heat to the surroundings, keeping the animal cool.

PORCUPINES

Grunting quietly to itself, an African porcupine is digging up roots for its evening feed. It is so busy that it does not hear the soft padding footsteps of the young leopard closing in behind it. The cat pounces, but instead of an easy meal it gets the shock of its life. With a snort of rage the porcupine raises its quills and charges backwards. Almost too late the leopard sees the danger. As it throws itself to one side, the needle-sharp quills miss its face by less than a metre.

All 22 species of porcupine have quills and spines. They are more obvious in some species than in others, and they come in many shapes and sizes. These quills and spines are highly modified hairs, providing their owners with a very effective defence.

SPECTACULAR QUILLS

The most spectacular of these specialized hairs are the 50cm black-and-white quills of the crested porcupines of Africa and Asia. They cover the animal's back from the shoulders to the tail, and they can be raised by muscles under the skin. They cannot be "shot" at attackers but they often stick in the face, neck or paws of an attacker and break off. They are not poisonous, but can become infected and so can cause serious injury.

The crested and brush-tailed porcupines of Africa and Asia also have clusters of tail quills modified into rattles. When the animal is frightened or cornered it shakes the tail to give a warning rattle. If that does not work, the African porcupine stamps its hind feet and grunts, and as a last resort charges its attacker.

The protective quills of the North American porcupine are different. They are only about 3cm long and are

PORCUPINES Hystricidae and Erethizontidae (*22 species*)

● ◪ ⌇

◪ **Habitat:** forest, open grassland, desert, rocky areas.

■ **Diet:** leaves, roots, fruits.

◎ **Breeding:** 1 or 2 young after pregnancy of about 210 days (North American porcupine), 93 days (Cape), 112 days (African).

Size: smallest (Prehensile-tailed porcupine): head-body 30cm, weight 900g; largest (crested porcupines): head-body 85cm, weight 27kg.

Colour: from black, white and grey, through yellow-brown to grey-brown.

Lifespan: up to 17 years.

Species mentioned in text:
African porcupine (*Hystrix cristata*)
Brush-tailed porcupines (*Atherurus* species)
Cape porcupine (*Hystrix africaeaustralis*)
Crested porcupines (*Hystrix* species)
Indonesian porcupines (*Thecarus* species)
North American porcupine (*Erethizon dorsatum*)
Prehensile-tailed porcupine (*Coendon prehensilis*)
South American tree porcupine (*C. bicolor*)

hidden in the animal's long coarse hair. They are very loosely fixed in the porcupine's skin, and an attacker is likely to find itself with nothing but a mouthful of hair and spines. To make things even more painful, the tips of the quills are covered in tiny barbs.

▼A Cape porcupine feeding on desert gourds. Most porcupines feed in this way, holding the food with their front paws and nibbling at it.

►A South American tree porcupine caught on the ground as it crosses from one tree to another. Just visible in the grass is the bare patch on the upper surface of the end of the tail. This patch of hard skin (the callus) helps to improve the grip of the prehensile tail.

▼Distant cousins Three members of the porcupine family from widely separated parts of the world. The North American porcupine (1) spends most of its time on the ground. The Indonesian porcupine (2) has a dense coat of flat, flexible spines. There are three species – in Borneo, Sumatra and the Philippines. The African porcupine (3) is one of five crested species. It is very adaptable and is found in desert, grassland and forest.

WORLDS APART

The porcupines are grouped in two large families. The Old World porcupines live in a wide range of habitats in Africa and Asia. New World porcupines are found in forest and grassland areas from northern Canada down to northern Argentina. The two groups have similar quills, teeth and jaw muscles. But scientists have still not worked out whether they are descendants of the same ancestors or whether evolution has come up with the same design in two separate families.

"OLD WORLD" SPECIES

All the Old World porcupines are ground-dwelling animals. They feed on roots, bulbs, fruits and berries, usually at night, either alone or in pairs. During the day they rest in caves, in holes among rocks or in burrows. Sometimes they take over old aardvark holes.

In many parts of Africa, porcupines are hunted for their arguably tasty meat. They are also killed by farmers because of their habit of raiding crops of maize, groundnuts, melons and potatoes. In spite of this, the porcupine is still common in Africa, probably because its natural enemies – lions, leopards and hyenas – are themselves becoming rare.

The sharp quills of the crested porcupines make mating rather dangerous, but somehow the animals manage. The young are born in a grass-lined chamber in a burrow or rock shelter, usually in summer. The babies are born with their eyes open. They are covered with fur and even have tiny soft quills which harden within a few hours.

The Cape porcupine of South Africa lives in family groups of up to eight. The older animals help to look after the babies, keeping close to young porcupines when they first start to feed outside the burrow at about 6 to 7 months.

IN THE AMERICAS

Unlike their Old World relatives, the porcupines of North and South America are mainly tree-dwellers. Their feet are equipped with large claws and hairless pads that provide a good grip. Most specialized of all are the Prehensile-tailed porcupine and the tree porcupines that live in the Central and South American forests. They have long muscular tails, which they can coil round branches to give extra support when climbing.

These animals too are nocturnal. They feed mainly on leaves, but also take fruits and seeds and sometimes come down to the ground to feed on roots and tubers. In winter, the North American porcupine feeds on pine needles, leaves and tree bark. It is especially fond of Red spruce and Sugar maple. In summer it often feeds on grasses and on roots, berries and flowers on the forest floor.

Destruction of South America's forests has placed several species in danger. The Prehensile-tailed porcupine is threatened in parts of Brazil. And the South American tree porcupine is listed as endangered by the Brazilian Academy of Science.

◄The Prehensile-tailed porcupine spends most of its time high in the trees. It is near-sighted, relying heavily on touch and smell.

►Despite its slowness, a hungry North American porcupine will sometimes climb 18-20m to reach young leaves.

CAPYBARA

The sight of a herd of capybara feeding quietly on the banks of the River Amazon is like a glimpse into prehistoric times. With their massive square heads and heavy bodies they look more like the primitive animals of 50 million years ago than modern members of the guinea-pig family. Yet that is exactly what they are. Members of the group keep in touch with one another with throaty purr sounds.

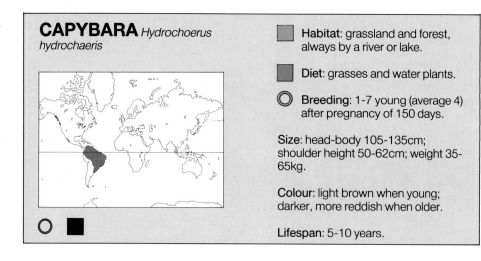

CAPYBARA *Hydrochoerus hydrochaeris*

Habitat: grassland and forest, always by a river or lake.

Diet: grasses and water plants.

Breeding: 1-7 young (average 4) after pregnancy of 150 days.

Size: head-body 105-135cm; shoulder height 50-62cm; weight 35-65kg.

Colour: light brown when young; darker, more reddish when older.

Lifespan: 5-10 years.

Capybaras are found only in South America, on the shores of rivers and lakes. They inhabit a wide variety of habitats, from open grassland to tropical rain forest. But no matter where they live, they are never very far from water.

They are big, heavy animals – the world's largest rodents – with barrel-shaped bodies and long shaggy coats. Their back legs are longer than their front legs, which gives them a lumbering, galloping run. Once in the water they are powerful swimmers. Their toes are partially webbed, and their eyes, ears and nostrils are high on the head so they remain clear of the water when swimming.

Capybaras head for the water at the first sign of danger. They can swim underwater for up to 5 minutes when trying to escape from a predator.

◀ The large hairless bump on the male capybara's snout is called the "morrillo". It is a gland that produces a sticky white liquid used as a scent-marker.

▼ The capybara's long back legs give it a rabbit-like shape when lying down.

▲ A male capybara leaving his tell-tale scent on a low branch by the river.

ALL-NIGHT DINERS

Capybaras are complete vegetarians. They eat a variety of water plants, but their main food is grass. They have large chisel-like front teeth and are efficient at cropping the short dry grass that remains after the dry season.

Mornings are usually spent resting, but as the temperature rises around midday the animals take to the water. Early evening is the main feeding time, but even after dark the capybara seldom sleeps for long. All through the night the animals are active, alternating short naps with spells of leisurely feeding.

BOSS OF A BAND

Capybaras live in bands or herds which vary in size throughout the year. A typical group will have one "boss" male, two or three females and their young, and perhaps two or three junior adult males. There is a clear order of rank among the males. The leader constantly reminds the juniors of his rank by chasing them around and by herding the females and young together.

In the wet season, groups vary in size between 10 and 40, but in the dry season bands of over 100 may gather round waterholes or in places with good grazing.

The capybara's main enemies are jaguars and caimans, but young ones are often taken by foxes, semi-wild dogs, eagles and vultures.

Capybaras start to breed when they are about 18 months old. Mating always takes place in the water. At the end of the long pregnancy the female leaves her group for a while, and the young are born in the cover of a long grass thicket. Within a few days they can walk and within a week they are feeding on grass.

COYPU

In the spring of 1988, British government officials announced that there were no longer any wild coypus living in the country's waterways. For more than 50 years this large, shaggy, South American river animal had made its home in the marshes and fens of the Norfolk Broads. But its river-bank burrowing and visits to sugar-beet fields had also made it many enemies. Eventually it was outlawed – and removed.

The coypu is a native of the rivers and marshes of central and southern parts of South America. It is a big, powerfully built rodent, which makes its home in a deep burrow tunnelled into the river bank. It is perfectly adapted for life in the water. Its coat is thick, waterproof and made of two layers. The long outer guard-hairs lock together when wet and help to trap a layer of air in the thick soft underfur beneath.

The coypu is an excellent swimmer, with fully webbed back feet. It feeds mainly on water plants, but often swims down to the river bed to add shellfish to its diet.

QUICK STARTERS

The coypu's young are born in a warm nest lined with grass, in a chamber at the end of the burrow. They are well covered with fur from the start and are born with their eyes open. The mother's milk is very rich, and the young grow quickly. Within a few days they can move about, and soon they are able to swim strongly.

Being able to move so soon after birth is very important. If the young were helpless for too long they would run the risk of drowning if the river level rose suddenly and water flooded into the nest chamber of the burrow.

The coypu is so specialized for life

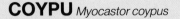

COYPU *Myocastor coypus*

 ● ■

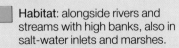
Habitat: alongside rivers and streams with high banks, also in salt-water inlets and marshes.

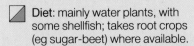
Diet: mainly water plants, with some shellfish; takes root crops (eg sugar-beet) where available.

Breeding: litters of up to 9 after pregnancy of 120-150 days.

Size: head-body 42-64cm; tail 25-45cm; weight 7-9kg.

Colour: dark brown to yellow-brown, with grey or white muzzle.

Lifespan: not known.

▶Wherever coypus have been farmed, some have escaped into the wild. This one was photographed in East Africa.

in the water that the mother can even suckle the young while swimming. The teats are placed high up on the sides of her body, just above the "water-line". There they can be seen and reached by young swimming alongside her or even by young riding on her back.

TOO SUCCESSFUL

In the 1920s and 1930s thousands of wild coypus were brought to Europe, the United States, Canada, Russia and Africa so that they could be bred for their valuable furs. Over the years some escaped. Others were released by their owners at times when business was bad. Wherever they were released, the coypus quickly made themselves at home. Soon they were more abundant in some of their new homes than in South America.

In Britain, for example, in the 1940s there were just a few coypus in one river in East Anglia. By 1972 the population had risen to about 12,000 and was rapidly becoming a problem. The animals' burrows were damaging river banks and ditches, and in some areas the coypus were also raiding crops such as sugar-beet. To stop the damage it was decided that the animals would have to be removed. Now there are no more coypu farms, and the wild coypus too are gone from the region.

▼ Many rodents are good swimmers, but the coypu, with its webbed feet and thick waterproof fur, is a truly aquatic animal.

▲ The coypu's fur is darkish brown-yellow. The outer hair is long and thick, covering the soft underfur beneath.

VISCACHAS AND CHINCHILLAS

High in the Andes mountains of Peru a scientist scans a rocky slope through binoculars. In a hollow between two boulders a small grey-brown animal is busy feeding on a patch of coarse grass. It looks like a cross between a squirrel and a large rabbit, but it is a mountain viscacha.

The viscachas and chinchillas are rodents, that is, members of the same huge animal group as rats, mice and porcupines. They inhabit some of the most remote parts of South America – the high mountains and grassland plains of Argentina, Chile, Bolivia and Peru. Yet their names are familiar to people who live thousands of kilometres away in New York, Paris and Tokyo. The reason is that the fur of these animals is in demand for expensive wraps and coats.

ONCE NEARLY EXTINCT

The chinchillas especially are prized for their soft, lightweight, blue-grey fur. But this sort of popularity had unfortunate results for the animals themselves. It takes over 150 pelts to make one full-length coat, and hunt- ing for the international fur trade brought the chinchillas to the brink of extinction. At the height of this trade, 100 years ago, over 200,000 chinchilla furs a year were sold in London auction-rooms alone.

Today, chinchillas are bred on special farms to provide furs for the luxury trade. This has taken some of the pressure off the remaining wild chinchillas, but they are still rare and listed as endangered.

MOUNTAIN HIGH-LIFE

As well as providing a home for the chinchillas, the rocky slopes of the

▼Young chinchillas, often kept as pets, are able to nibble plants less than an hour after they are born.

VISCACHAS AND CHINCHILLAS
Chinchillidae (*6 species*)

○ ■ ☠

▲ **Habitat:** rocky slopes at high altitude; Argentinian pampas.

■ **Diet:** plant leaves, stems and seeds; mosses and lichens.

◖ **Breeding:** chinchilla: 1-6 young after pregnancy of 111 days; Plains viscacha: 1-4 young after 154 days.

Size: chinchilla: head-body 22-38cm, weight 0.5-0.8kg; Plains viscacha: head-body 47-66cm, weight 4-8kg.

Colour: grey, blue-grey or brown, white or yellow-white undersides.

Lifespan: up to 10 years (chinchilla).

Species mentioned in text:
Chinchillas (*Chinchilla* species)
Plains viscacha (*Lagostomus maximus*)
Mountain viscachas (*Lagidium* species)

high Andes mountains also support three kinds of mountain viscacha. These hardy little animals can live as high as 4,900m, feeding during the day on the stems and seeds of coarse mountain grasses, and on the mosses and lichens that grow on the rocks.

Mountain viscachas live in colonies of up to 80 animals, using natural holes and spaces among the rocks as shelter from the wind and cold. They are very sociable animals and often cuddle up to each other when sitting out in the Sun.

They communicate with whistling calls. A long note signals that a large

▼ A viscacha mother and young. Females reach maturity when 2 years old, but males mature in 7 months.

animal such as a human or dog or sheep is near by. Most of the animals "freeze" and wait to see what happens next. Others climb higher to get a better view. A short sharp call is the signal that a hawk has been spotted. This immediately sends every animal diving for the safety of a hole among the rocks.

Female mountain viscachas may produce young up to three times in a year, but they usually have only one baby at a time. Food is scarce in the mountains, and it is unlikely that a female could produce enough milk to feed more than one.

PAMPAS LOW-LIFE
Down on the vast plains of the Argentinian pampas lives the much bigger Plains viscacha. Males weigh up

to 8kg (ten times as much as a chinchilla) and females about 4kg. The viscachas live in underground burrow systems called *viscacheros*. Each group of 15-30 animals is led by a senior male and may contain animals of several generations.

Unlike its mountain cousins, the Plains viscacha is most active at night. It leaves the burrow as evening falls and feeds on any vegetation it can find. A group will strip the ground over the burrow completely bare – 10 viscachas eat as much as a sheep, and their acidic urine destroys pasture – which may help them to see foxes and other predators in good time. The Plains viscacha also has the odd habit of collecting sticks, stones and bits of bone and piling them in heaps over the burrow entrances.

MOLE-RATS AND ROOT RATS

It is midday in the Sun-baked landscape of Ethiopia. A group of biologists seek shade to avoid the blistering 60°C heat. Yet just 20cm beneath their feet a "chain-gang" of small, hairless, burrowing animals are hard at work on a new feeding tunnel. They toil away in a pitch-dark world where the temperature remains at a steady 30°C. This is the world of the Naked mole-rat.

▼**The mole-rat chain gang** Naked mole-rats are organized rather like bees and ants, with different groups doing different jobs. "Workers" dig new tunnels. Each mole-rat takes a turn digging at the front, then pushes the loose earth backwards up the tunnel. The animal then works its way back to the front of the line by stepping over its team-mates. At the exit hole, a "kicker" mole-rat shoves out the earth.

MOLE-RATS AND ROOT RATS
Bathyergidae and Rhizomyinae
(*15 species*)

○ ◨

● **Habitat:** underground burrows in sand and various different soils.

▨ **Diet:** roots, tubers, some species also herbs and grass.

○ **Breeding:** litters of about 12 after pregnancy of 70 days (Naked mole-rat, details of Common mole-rat and others unknown).

Size: smallest (Naked mole-rat): head-body 9-12cm, weight 30-60g; largest (Dune mole-rat): head-body to 30cm, weight 750-1,800g; root rats larger.

Colour: dark brown to light brown, Naked mole-rat pale pink colour.

Lifespan: to 10 years in captivity.

Species mentioned in text:
Common mole-rat (*Cryptomys hottentotus*)
Dune mole-rat (*Bathyergus suillus*)
East African root rat (*Tachyoryctes splendens*)
Naked mole-rat (*Heterocephalus glaber*)

Mole-rats live across most of Africa south of the Sahara Desert. They are found in many different habitats, wherever there is soft soil or sand for them to burrow in.

TUNNELLING RATS
The mole-rats are rodents that have become completely adapted to life below ground. Their bodies are almost cylindrical in shape, to fit into their tunnels. Their eyes are tiny, and they can close their nostrils to keep out the soil as they dig.

The most unusual thing about these animals is the digging method they use. Most burrowers dig with spade-like front feet, but mole-rats dig with their enormous front teeth. As the animal chisels its way through the soil, it pulls the loose earth under its body with its front feet, then pushes it back with its hind feet.

LIFE IN THE DARK
Because they live in complete darkness, the mole-rats depend mainly on their senses of touch and smell to find food and communicate with each other. Most of them have very sensitive hairs scattered over the body to help them feel their surroundings. For the Naked mole-rat these are the animal's only hairs.

Mole-rats live on roots and on the underground tubers and bulbs that

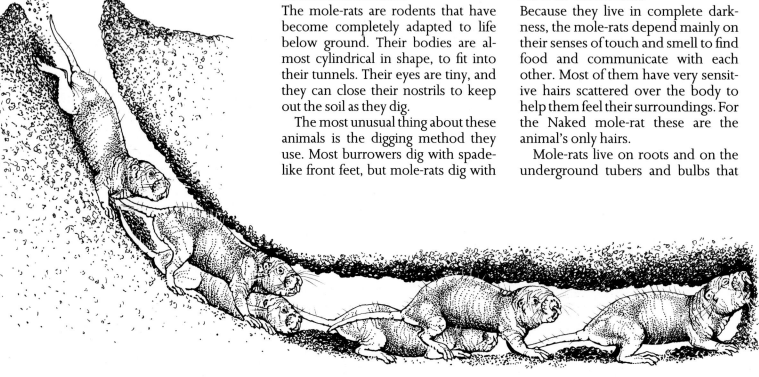

plants use as food stores. They gnaw large tubers where they are and leave them to continue growing. They collect smaller ones, storing them in underground larders.

Mole-rats collect all their food in the tunnel system, which also contains resting rooms and toilet chambers. The systems can be up to 1km long.

UNDERGROUND TEAMWORK

The odd one out in the mole-rat group is the Naked mole-rat. Most species live alone or in small groups, but the Naked mole-rat lives in colonies of up to 80 animals. Only one pair breeds. The rest are organized as "workers", who dig tunnels and collect food, or "assistants", who look after the nest and the breeding female.

▲The young Naked mole-rat is suckled only by the mother. Later it is fed on plant food by all the colony members.

▼The East African root rat belongs to a different family from mole-rats, but it has the same life-style.

RABBITS AND HARES

In the late afternoon of a spring day, a male and female hare face each other at the edge of a field. For several minutes they glare at each other without moving. Suddenly the female hare leaps right over the male, giving him a vicious two-footed drop-kick as she goes by. The male hare spins round and kicks back. Then the two animals drop back on their haunches and sit upright, face to face, cuffing and boxing furiously with their forepaws. Eventually the male decides he has had enough. He turns to run. But even as he dives for the safety of the nearby hedge, the female victor gets in one last kick.

The "mad March hares" that perform such crazy antics during the mating season belong to one of the world's most successful animal groups. The common European rabbit is the most familiar rabbit of open fields and grasslands, but it has cousins that live in the snow-covered Arctic wilderness, and others that live in deserts and tropical forests and even on the tops of mountains.

ACROSS THE GLOBE

World wide there are 44 species of rabbit and hare. There are native species in North America and parts of South America, all over Africa and right across Europe and Asia. Some parts of South America, and all of Australia and New Zealand, originally had no native rabbits and hares, but European animals were taken there by settlers and very quickly made themselves at home. In Australia the European rabbit is still a pest. Only Antarctica and the huge island of Madagascar are completely without rabbits and hares.

RABBITS AND HARES Leporidae (*44 species*)

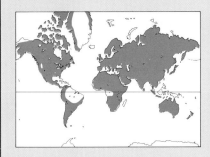

○

◼ **Habitat:** virtually everywhere, from coast fields, grassland and forest to desert and high mountains.

◼ **Diet:** grass, leaves, bark; also crops and tree seedlings.

◎ **Breeding:** rabbits: litters of 3-12, up to 5 times a year, after pregnancy of 30-40 days; hares: litters of 1-9, up to 4 times a year, after pregnancy of up to 50 days; northern species mainly spring/summer; others breed throughout year.

Size: smallest (Pygmy rabbit): head-body 25-30cm, weight 0.3kg; largest (European hare): head-body 50-76cm, weight 5kg.

Colour: reddish-brown through brown, buff and grey to white; Arctic species change from brown to white in winter.

Lifespan: usually less than 1 year; domestic (pet) rabbits up to 18 years.

Species mentioned in text:
Arctic hare (*Lepus timidus*)
Black-tailed jackrabbit (*L. californicus*)
Bushman hare (*Bunolagus monticularis*)
Cottontails (*Sylvilagus* species)
European hare (*Lepus europaeus*)
European rabbit (*Oryctolagus cuniculus*)
Hispid hare (*Caprolagus hispidus*)
Pygmy rabbit (*Sylvilagus idahoensis*)
Snowshoe hare (*Lepus americanus*)
Sumatran hare (*Nesolagus netscheri*)
Volcano rabbit (*Romerolagus diazi*)

▶ **Rabbits and hares of the world** The Hispid hare (**1**) is an endangered species from India. It seldom leaves the shelter of the forest. Volcano rabbit of Mexico (**2**) shown sitting in the long grass recycling its droppings. The European hare in its "boxing" position (**3**). Greater red rock-hare (*Pronolagus crassicaudatus*) (**4**) of Southern Africa in alert posture. Male Eastern cottontail (*Sylvilagus floridanus*) (**5**) in alert posture.

10

9

◄The very rare Sumatran hare (6) grooming its muzzle and spreading scent from scent glands. Bunyoro rabbit (*Poelagus marjorita*)(7) hopping along. The species is common in parts of Central and Eastern Africa. Adult male European rabbbit (8) scratching his chin. Bushman hare (9) of the Southern African river banks, now an endangered species. The Amami rabbit (*Pentalagus furnessi*) (10) is found on just two small Japanese islands. The total population is about 5,000, and the species has protected status.

FLEET OF FOOT

Rabbits and hares are very similar in shape, though they vary in size. They have long soft fur, which covers the whole body including the feet, and a small furry tail which is usually white, or at least white underneath. The tail is always turned upwards, so that as the animal runs, the white fur may act as a target for predators, keeping them away from vital areas of its body. The animal's alarm signal is to thump its back feet on the ground.

The front legs are quite short but strong, and the five toes on each forefoot have sharp claws for digging. The back legs are very much longer and are clearly designed for running and bounding over open ground. Some of the largest hares can reach speeds up to 80kph when fleeing from danger.

Both rabbits and hares have large eyes, placed high on the sides of the head. They give clear vision in twilight and at night, which is when many species are most active. The position of the eyes also gives the animals very good vision to the sides, and even above and behind them. This is very important to an animal that makes such a tasty and tempting target for eagles, wild cats, polecats and a host of other predators.

FOOD PROCESSING

Rabbits and hares live entirely on plant food, mainly grasses, leaves, bark and roots. Like the rodents, they have two large front teeth which grow continuously. But they differ from rats and mice by having a second, much smaller pair of front teeth tucked in behind the main pair.

Their internal organs too are especially developed to cope with large amounts of low-quality vegetable food. The ground-up food passes into the stomach, and then into the gut. But instead of passing straight out through the last section of the gut it is held for a while in another stomach-like bag where bacteria help to break down the coarse food more thoroughly.

Rabbits and hares produce two kinds of dropping. When the animal is most active, normal firm dry droppings are left, often in special "latrine" areas. But when the animal is resting, much softer droppings are produced. These are eaten again and recycled through the digestive system for a second time so that useful chemicals such as vitamin B can be absorbed into the animal's body.

Because rabbits breed very quickly, and can eat a great variety of food, they can easily become a nuisance. In some areas they are "public enemy number one" for farmers and foresters. In the United States, for example, Black-tailed jackrabbits cause widespread damage to crops in California, while the cottontails and the Snowshoe hare can ruin new forestry plantations by nipping the growing shoots off the tender young tree seedlings.

BURROWS AND HOLLOWS

The biggest differences between rabbits and hares can be seen in their choice of where to live and in the way they bring up their young.

Most rabbits live in underground burrow systems called warrens. The young rabbits (kittens) are born in a warm nest, snugly lined with hair and soft grass, either in the main warren or in a nursery burrow near by. They are hairless, and their eyes do not open for several days (10 days for European rabbits). The female (doe) feeds her young for only a few minutes in each 24 hours. She then seals them in by covering the burrow entrance with earth, and goes off to feed.

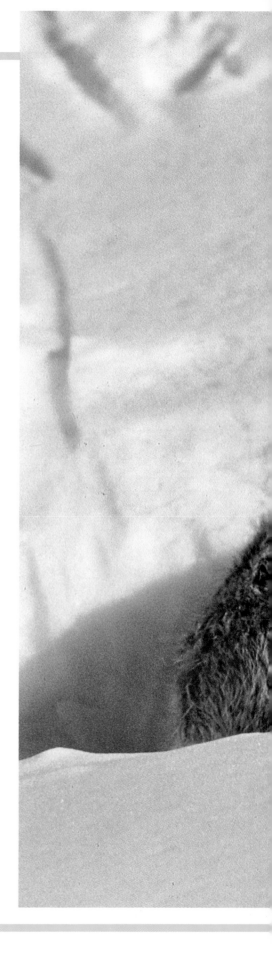

▶Many northern species, like this jackrabbit, shed their fur in the autumn and replace their light brown summer coat with a much thicker, warmer, winter coat of white.

►Outside the breeding season, the European hare is a shy, quiet animal. But all that changes in the spring. As the mating instinct takes over, the males (bucks) and females (does) become aggressive and quite outrageous in their behaviour. They dash about, leaping into the air, fighting and chasing each other. As each male tries to mate with a female that is ready to breed, she rejects the advances of any male she considers unworthy.

▼Two-week-old European rabbits in the burrow where they were born. These kittens have opened their eyes for the first time, but have not yet seen the outside world.

The young rabbits do not venture outside for about 3 weeks.

Hares are very different. Only a few of them make burrows of any kind. Usually they rest in a shallow hollow, called a form, in soft earth or in long grass. The young hares (leverets) are well developed at birth. They are covered with warm fur, and their eyes are open. When they are just 2-3 days old the mother places each one in a separate form, well hidden among rocks or tall grass. There they remain until the family meets up, usually around sunset, for the one feed of the day. Because they live out in the open, young hares can run almost from birth. Their main protection, how-

ever, is to remain absolutely still.

With so many different species, living in so many different habitats it is not surprising to find that not every one follows these "rules". A number of hares do make burrows. Black-tailed jackrabbits, for example, sometimes dig short burrows to escape from the fierce summer heat in the American deserts. Arctic hares in Scotland may dig burrows for their young to use in times of danger. Not all rabbits dig burrows either. Many of the cottontails either use holes made by other animals or simply hide themselves among thick vegetation.

THE NUMBERS EXPLOSION

European rabbits are famous for the speed at which they reproduce. Females often produce five litters in a year, each of 5 or 6 young (occasionally up to 12). Each young female, in turn, will be ready to produce her own first family by the time she is 3 months old. At that rate it is no surprise that rabbits can quickly become a major pest.

Hares do not multiply quite so quickly, but they too are fast breeders. The European hare was taken to Argentina in 1888. In just 100 years it has spread throughout the whole

◀In sandy soils, rabbits can easily dig new burrows. But in areas of hard soil, like this chalky bank, the best burrow sites are prized possessions.

country. It is now found spread over 3 million sq km. In the central pampas region, 5-10 million hares are caught each year for their light meat.

RARE RABBIT RELATIVES

The family that contains one of the most common animals on Earth also includes several surprisingly rare species. Some are on the international list of endangered species.

One of the rarest is the Sumatran hare, which inhabits the remote mountain forests of the South-east Asian island of Sumatra. Only 20 have ever been seen, and only one has been seen in the last 10 years. If the forests are cut for their valuable timber, this unusual striped hare will disappear for ever.

In the sal forests of northern India and Bangladesh, the Hispid hare is also becoming more and more rare. Its woodland habitat is being destroyed to make way for cattle grazing. The Bushman hare of Southern Africa faces a similar threat. Its natural habitat is the dense vegetation along river banks, but these are also the most fertile areas and so they are being taken over by farmers, leaving the hares with nowhere to go.

Strangest of all is the case of the Volcano rabbit, which lives at 3,000-4,000m on the flanks of two volcanic mountain ranges near Mexico City. It is one of the world's smallest rabbits, and lives in groups of up to five animals in burrows among open pine-woods and grassy slopes. It is active mainly during the day, using a variety of calls to keep in touch with one another. Unfortunately the 17 million people of Mexico City are barely half an hour's drive away, so the rabbits are threatened now by hunters and noisy tourists as well as by destruction of their habitat.

INDEX

237

PICTURE CREDITS

Key: t top, b bottom, c centre, l left, r right.

Abbreviations: A Ardea. AN Agence Nature. ANT Australasian Nature Transparencies. BCL Bruce Coleman Ltd. FL Frank Lane Agency. FS Fiona Sunquist. GF George Frame. J Jacana. NHPA Natural History Photographic Agency. OSF Oxford Scientific Films. PEP Planet Earth Pictures. SAL Survival Anglia Ltd.